Campden & Chorleywood Food
Research Association Group

Chipping Campden
Gloucestershire
GL55 6LD UK
Tel: +44 (0) 1386 842000
Fax: +44 (0) 1386 842100
www.campden.co.uk

Guideline No. 28

An Introduction to the Practice of Microbiological Risk Assessment for Food Industry Applications

Phil Voysey

2000

Campden & Chorleywood Food Research Association Group comprises
Campden & Chorleywood Food Research Association
and its subsidiary companies
CCFRA Technology Ltd CCFRA Group Services Ltd Campden & Chorleywood Magyarország, Hungary

ISBN: 0 905942 33 7

PREFACE

The technique of Risk Assessment has been used effectively to assess and manage risks in Chemistry and Engineering for a number of years. It is only comparatively recently, however, that the technique has been applied to food safety, and microbiology in particular. The living nature of foodborne pathogens makes the application of Microbiological Risk Assessment (MRA) more difficult.

Previous MRA guides have usually been written by governmental and regulatory bodies. The Codex Alimentarius Commission and the European Union have produced draft guidelines on how to carry out an MRA, which are aimed for applications at a government level in international trade. Our intention in producing this document, is to provide a simple and straightforward guide to MRA, for use by the food industry, which follows the guidelines laid down by Codex and the EU.

At first sight, carrying out an MRA might appear a daunting task, similar in difficulty to the first HACCP exercises. However, the reader is encouraged to face an MRA with a "can do" attitude. In fact MRAs are probably already being carried out throughout the food industry, just not in a formal manner. Formalisation will improve the quality, consistency, and transparency of decisions made, and the ability of the study to include new data and cope with new threats. Specific examples of areas where MRA might be applied are product and process development.

Whilst we recognise that the undertaking of a formal MRA is a role for governmental bodies, responsible food companies will wish to undertake as many elements of MRA as possible in order to enhance the safe production, distribution and retail of food.

MRA as described in this document is a flexible tool. It can be used with different levels of sophistication, and is therefore of use to companies of all sizes. Any assessment requires input from a number of disciplines, just as HACCP does. An MRA can help to target research needs for a particular product range or food manufacturing company. Another function of an MRA is to strengthen the Hazard Analysis part of HACCP. The purpose of this document is to introduce and describe the process of MRA, such that the user is informed in how to undertake an MRA

Microbiological Risk Assessment is a rapidly developing area. This first document will need to be reviewed and updated in time, as the discipline evolves.

P. A. Voysey
June 2000

CCFRA WORKING PARTY

Dr. Jonathan Back	-	MAFF/Food Standards Agency
Mr. Stephen Batchford	-	Sainsbury's Supermarkets plc
Ms Christelle Billon	-	Unilever Research
Prof. Martyn Brown	-	Unilever Research
Dr. Paul Cook	-	Department of Health/Food Standards Agency
Prof. Richard Gilbert	-	PHLS
Dr. David Jervis	-	Unigate
Mr. Keith Jewell	-	CCFRA
Mr. Damian Killen	-	H.J. Heinz
Mr. Derrick Kilsby	-	Unilever Research (Chair)
Dr. Robert Mitchell	-	PHLS
Dr. Mike Stringer	-	CCFRA
Dr. Phil Voysey	-	CCFRA (Editor)
Dr. Clive Woolley	-	RHM Technology

EXECUTIVE SUMMARY

Risk Assessment is one of three parts of the technique of Risk Analysis. The other two parts are Risk Management and Risk Communication. Risk Assessment is a scientifically-based process including the following steps: hazard identification; hazard characterisation; exposure assessment; and risk characterisation. Microbiological Risk Assessment (MRA) concerns itself with the hazards presented by foodborne pathogens or their toxins. As far as this document is concerned, the physical matrix in which the hazard is situated is a food.

The objective of carrying out an MRA is to find out the level of risk associated with a food. How this risk will be managed and communicated to stakeholders will not be specifically addressed by this document. It is important to note at this stage, however, that Risk Assessment should not be influenced by Risk Management or Risk Communication.

The principal benefit of MRA is that it allows objective comparison and assessment of different risks. MRA is complementary to HACCP, as it assists with the identification and prioritisation of hazards. Food safety management is dependent on the choice of hazard. MRA can be used as a means of selecting hazards for consideration in a HACCP process. Because it is formal and transparent, MRA allows communication of risk decisions to customers, regulators and manufacturing staff.

The aim of this document is to outline the principles of MRA and give examples of studies to demonstrate how they may be put into practice. These examples cover quantitative and qualitative (including comparative) MRAs. The examples include both infectious microorganisms and toxin producers.

This document gives examples of MRAs of different complexities. In its most 'complex' form, the risk may be expressed **quantitatively**, for example, a 1 in 10^{12} chance of dying from food poisoning caused by microorganism x in food y. Currently in the food industry, the risk is likely to be expressed in a simpler form such as a category - for example, 'negligible', 'low' or 'high' risk, or by comparison (**comparative** MRA) of one product with another. These are examples of **qualitative** MRAs. An example of a **comparative** MRA output would be "the risk associated with food *q* is less than that with food *r*." Qualitative MRAs can be carried out with more limited data and less (available) resources, which will probably be the case with most food manufacturing concerns.

CONTENTS

HOW TO USE THIS GUIDE

This document is written to be used as a reference guide or hand-book rather than a book to be read from cover to cover in one sitting. It has two main parts plus two appendices.

Part One

This gives general information about Microbiological Risk Assessment (MRA). It is intended as general background reading material and it should be read before Part Two is tackled. It first addresses the following aspects of MRA:

- why it is important;
- what it does,
- what it does not do;
- the benefits of MRA;
- background information and history; and
- how it interacts with other quality systems.

This part also provides a list of definitions of specific terms used in this guide (Section 1.6), which can also be consulted when carrying out an MRA, and a description of each of the 9 principles of MRA.

Part Two

This is designed as a guide to performing an MRA. It is laid out in a step-by-step manner, so that the reader is taken through the processes of the MRA in a logical way. Technical information and examples to help with carrying out MRAs are given. Different parts will be of interest to the different members of the team carrying out the MRA, therefore not all information will be of direct relevance to all team members. Coverage in this part includes a description of the step concerned, a detailed commentary on the sub-steps involved and, through a series of landscape tables, an extended illustration of the information required when conducting an MRA. The latter includes reference to two published examples of MRAs, to make the illustrations as tangible as possible.

This part of the manual is a reference guide, designed to be dipped into step-by-step while working through the development of an MRA. However, it is suggested that an overall 'light perusal' of this part, in advance of starting the risk assessment, would be beneficial and make development of the MRA easier.

Appendix 1

This shows the relationship between governmental and food company safety activities.

Appendix 2

This provides a method for performing a Risk Profile, which is a simple paper-based approach to Risk Assessment. The technique contains all the elements of a risk assessment, but utilises information which can be chosen from tables of values representing the likely ranges for the key determinants of risk. This by-passes to some extent "expert opinion" which may not be readily accessed by some small and medium-sized companies. It must be stressed that, to carry out an MRA, input from expert microbiologists is essential and that the output of the profile will only be as good as the data used.

The risk profile allows the user to recognise the features of the product and process in question, in terms of which is exerting the biggest influence on the level of risk. It also helps to put into context the seriousness of various hazards and allows the user to 'visualise' the "riskiness" of the product under examination. In short, the 'Risk Profile' approach can provide a quick and useful overall impression of the risks associated with a product or process, and is useful as a first step in risk assessment. It will not, and cannot, however, give the detail obtained by carrying out a formal MRA.

PART 1

GENERAL INFORMATION ON RISK ASSESSMENT

SECTION 1 - INTRODUCTION AND HISTORY OF MRA

1.1 Why Risk Assessment is Important

Microbiological risk assessment (MRA) can be used as a basis for improving food safety and choice. Adopting MRA can significantly benefit your business. When used alongside a hazard analysis and control system like HACCP, it enables companies to minimise the risks associated with identified microbiological hazards. Ultimately, then, it will provide a very powerful tool for responsible food and drink companies to help protect their customers and consumers and, by implication, improve their brand image and business activities. Moreover, in the event that a problem should arise, a full and thorough MRA could provide a valuable component of a due diligence defence.

MRA is now gaining international recognition. It will, in the foreseeable future, be as widely accepted and adopted as HACCP currently is, in helping to assure food safety. This guide therefore sets out to do two things. Firstly, it provides a basic introduction to the concepts of MRA - what it is, what it is not, what it can do for your business, and how it relates to other quality systems. It then follows this with a structured step-by-step guide on how to undertake a microbiological risk assessment from start to finish.

1.2 Scope

MRA is a powerful tool which can be applied to a range of simple and complex supply chain operations. It is not confined to large food manufacturers, or governmental or regulatory bodies. The complexity of MRA that can be considered (quantitative or qualitative), make its use applicable to all stages of the food chain. The effects of raw material sourcing and supply, storage, processing, distribution, consumer usage, and so on, will all have an effect on the risk of a hazard being realised, and this can be gauged using MRA.

MRA can be used as a basis for designing new products or processes or to reduce the risk from an existing product or process. In this and other ways, MRA can be used to minimise food safety issues associated with foods.

The aim of this document is to outline the principles of MRA and give examples of studies to demonstrate how they may be put into practice. These examples cover quantitative and qualitative (including comparative) MRAs. The examples include both infectious microorganisms and toxin producers.

1.3 Relationship of Risk Assessment with Risk Analysis

The Risk Analysis framework consists of a number of activities including Risk Assessment, Risk Management and Risk Communication. The scientific part, requiring input from microbiologists, is Risk Assessment. It is this part which is being addressed here. Risk Assessment involves dealing with knowledge of and information relating to microorganisms, and other aspects where microbiology is the key subject area. Although microbiologists have input into Risk Management and Risk Communication, they do not necessarily lead it. The inter-relationship between Risk Assessment, Risk Management and Risk Communication is illustrated in Figure 1.

Figure 1 - Risk Analysis Framework
(Lammerding, 1996)

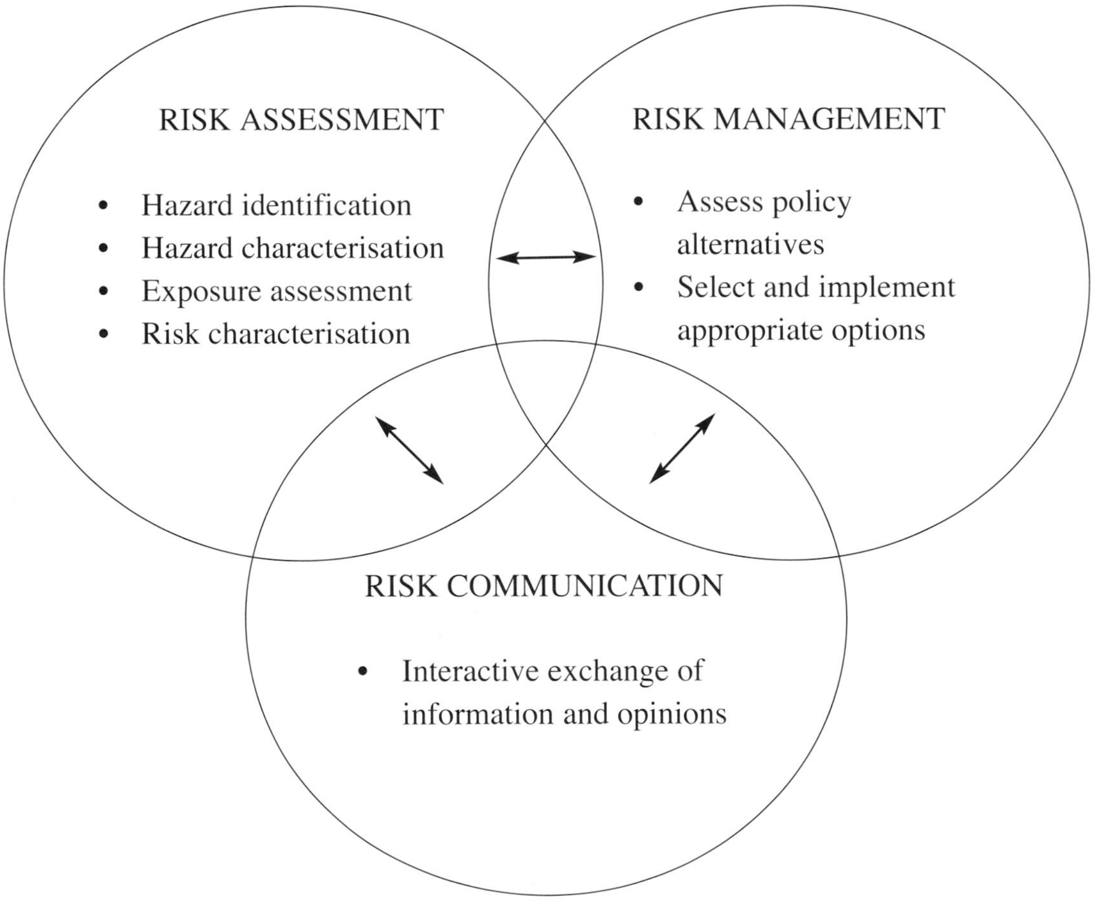

1.4 Benefits

The benefits of using MRA are many and varied. Key benefits include:

Decision making

- The structured approach of MRA makes your decision-making **transparent** and **effective**.
- MRA can be used to identify where there is **uncertainty** about the risks associated with your operation.
- MRA can identify those factors which have the most influence on the level of risk. MRA is complementary to and acts as a basis for HACCP, which is the food safety **control** tool.

Risk management

- MRA provides guidance on the cost effective control of foodborne hazards, because it allows them to be **prioritised**.
- MRA is complementary to **HACCP**.
- MRA can help you to demonstrate **compliance** with risk-based legislation to regulators and to your customers.
- MRA is internationally accepted and will facilitate **international** trade.
- MRA can be used to assess **any safety risk in any food** at **any part of the food chain**.
- MRA can be used to assess both actual and theoretical safety risks designed into a product or those arising during manufacture, and can therefore be used to **predict** potential problems.

Risk communication

- Because it is transparent, MRA allows risk decisions and their basis to be communicated to customers, to regulators and to staff.
- MRA can be used as an aid for training.
- MRA can be used in the process of setting specifications.

1.5 Risk Assessment in Context

In recent years, considerable effort has ben expended in developing techniques for controlling microbiological food safety, which provide more objective assessments of hazards and risks. Food microbiologists have attempted to more fully understand product and process interactions and identify areas of potential concern and priorities for control, thus adopting a more pro-active approach to assuring the microbiological safety of food.

In June 1996, the UK Government's Advisory Committee on Dangerous Pathogens (ACDP) published a document entitled "Microbiological Risk Assessment: an Interim Report". The report set out, in general terms, the principles of risk assessment as applied to microbiology in relation to public health issues. The report stated that the relatively slow development of microbiological risk assessment is in part a consequence of the complex nature of the risks posed by microorganisms.

In August 1996, Codex published, via its Committee on Food Hygiene, "Principles and Guidelines for the Application of Microbiological Risk Assessment". (These principles have also been published by European bodies.) The Codex document was a draft document produced for further discussion. In January 1997, a new European Union Scientific Co-operation Task (SCOOP) was established on MRA for foodborne pathogens. The task, which was co-ordinated by France, ran for two years, and focused on how data is collated for MRA. The project aimed to provide a template for structured data gathering to assist future work on MRA at the European level.

In 1998, the International Life Sciences Institute (ILSI) Europe published a monograph entitled "Food Safety Management Tools" - a document describing the tools currently available for food safety management and a framework for their interaction and use.

In summary, a number of initiatives are being taken to develop the field of MRA. It is important to recognise that this is an analytical process based on technical information and statistical probabilities. Whereas technical experts deal with science-based risk assessments, the lay-public is very much focused on risk perception. These perceptions may have no correlation with the severity of the actual risk and may be influenced by a degree of choice, control and derived benefits of the risks seen by the consumer. The quality of a risk assessment will only be as good as the data considered which goes into the calculation and hence much development effort is being focused on data needs and data generation.

The ACDP defined risk analysis as the "structured" approach to the reduction of risk. It includes risk assessment, risk management and risk communication. The relationship between these three aspects of risk analysis are indicated diagrammatically in Figure 1.

It will readily be appreciated that a formal risk analysis is a complex process involving an interaction of the three key elements of assessment, management and communication. Whilst it is most desirable for risk assessment to be based on quantitative data, this may not always be possible and hence qualitative judgements or opinion may be used.

1.6 Definition of Terms

Assumption : An expert judgement made on the basis of incomplete information, which therefore has uncertainty associated with it.

Dose-response assessment : Determining the relationship between the exposure of a consumer to a hazard (dose) and the severity and/or frequency of associated adverse health effects (response).

Exposure assessment : An assessment of the likely intake of hazards with a food. Ideally this should be quantitative, but can be qualitative.

Food safety objective : A government-defined target considered necessary to protect the health of consumers (this may apply to raw materials, a process or finished products). (ILSI, 1998a)

Hazard : A biological, chemical or physical agent in food with the potential to cause an adverse health effect.

Hazard characterisation : An assessment of the nature of the adverse health effects associated with a hazard which may be present in foods. Ideally this should be quantitative, but can be qualitative. Where possible, a dose-response assessment should be performed, although data may not always be available for biological or physical agents.

Hazard identification : The process of identifying and describing the hazards that are likely to be present in a food or group of foods.

Quantitative risk assessment : A Risk Assessment that provides numerical expressions of risk and indication of the attendant uncertainties. (Codex, 1998)

Qualitative risk assessment	:	A Risk Assessment based on data which, whilst forming an inadequate basis for numerical risk estimate, nonetheless, when conditioned by prior expert knowledge and identification of attendant uncertainties, permits risk ranking (comparison) or separation into descriptive categories of risk. (Codex, 1998).
Risk	:	The likelihood of the hazard causing an adverse health effect, which also considers the likely severity of that effect.
Risk analysis	:	A process consisting of three components: risk assessment, risk management and risk communication.
Risk assessment	:	A scientifically based process consisting of the following steps:- (i) hazard identification (ii) hazard characterisation (iii) exposure assessment and (iv) risk characterisation To carry out an MRA, the additional steps of **statement of purpose** and **production of a formal report** need to be addressed (Notermans *et al.*, 1996). This document proposes that a further step **outline MRA** (Step 0) is carried out in addition. Consequently, the steps making up a formal MRA are: STEP 0 Outline MRA STEP 1 Statement of purpose STEP 2 Hazard identification STEP 3 Exposure assessment STEP 4 Hazard characterisation STEP 5 Risk characterisation STEP 6 Formal report
Risk characterisation	:	An estimation of the likelihood of adverse health effects occurring in given consumers, and their severity, based on hazard identification and exposure assessment. The estimate should ideally be quantitative, but can be qualitative. The degree of uncertainty must be specified.

Risk communication : The discussion of risk among risk assessors, risk managers, consumers and other interested parties, and communication of the output of the risk assessment.

Risk management : The process of weighing alternatives in the light of the results of risk assessment and, if required, selecting and implementing appropriate controls.

Risk profile : This is a simple paper-based approach to Risk Assessment. The technique contains all the elements of a risk assessment, but utilises information which can be chosen from tables of values representing the likely ranges for the key determinants of risk.

Uncertainty (of a value, an assumption, or a conclusion) : An indication of the range of values that are consistent with all of the observations, data and expert judgement, and that with varying degrees of credibility can be attributed to the value, assumption or conclusion.

Note that the uncertainty is **not** expressed as the confidence in the basis of the value/assumption/conclusion, but as the range of alternatives that might be true.

Examples:

- Average process temperature = 121°C±0.5°C (95% confidence interval)
- Individual process temperature =
- 121°C±3°C (95% confidence interval).

Variability : An indication of the range of individual values that are expressed as a summary value.

Examples:

- 95% of individual process temperatures are within ± 2°C of the target.
- Levels of contamination vary between 10^2 and 10^5/g.

SECTION 2 - MRA AND OTHER QUALITY SYSTEMS

2.1 Introduction

MRA is a scientific approach to estimating risk and understanding the factors that influence it. The primary purpose of MRA is to evaluate and document the available scientific evidence for a given pre-determined hazard. It can be an important part of any comprehensive food safety programme.

HACCP is the foremost system for the control of microbiological hazards in food. HACCP should focus on those operations (Practices, Procedures and Processes, etc.) which can be managed so that a desired level of safety (with an acceptable risk) can be attained. MRA can assist in the hazard analysis process of any HACCP plan to determine which hazards require the necessary control to ensure the production/manufacture of safe products.

Unlike HACCP, which identifies hazards and the appropriate controls, MRA will quantify a hazard and its ultimate effect on the consumer. The control system (HACCP) and risk assessment (MRA) are intimately linked and can interact in both directions, i.e. it is possible that hazards can be identified as significant by means of either system. HACCP alone deals with the control options for a specific process.

The management of food safety is much more effective if underpinned by a comprehensive quality system (e.g. ISO 9000). There is often confusion over the roles of these different systems in a food safety management programme. For further explanation of this see Appendix 1. MRA can contribute at various levels to all these activities.

2.2 Quality Policy

The company quality system will include a policy statement document. Risk Analysis should be included in the policy. It is essential that this is supported by a management structure empowered to implement these requirements.

2.3 Quality Document

HACCP is an integral part of the quality system. When it is supported by MRA, the output from the MRA should also be included in the quality documentation.

2.4 Quality Review

The quality system should be designed to ensure that all factors that influence it are highlighted and that a suitable review mechanism is in place. Most current systems are set up so that any changes to the process, product or environment are identified, and these must then drive a review of the MRA. The quality system must also include a requirement to periodically review the scientific data on which the MRA was based.

SECTION 3 - MRA PRINCIPLES

The system of MRA consists of a number of principles. There are eleven given in the latest Codex Alimentarius Commission draft (1998). These have been reduced to nine by the European Commission (1997). In reducing the number to nine, the EC did not exclude any of the information included by Codex. The principles as defined by the EC are outlined below:

Principle 1 **Risk Assessment for microbiological hazards must be soundly based on science**

All available scientific data relevant to the risk assessment should be considered. If the data being used is poor, the level of uncertainty will be high. The information used and the conclusions drawn must be recorded, to allow the basis and uncertainty/reliability of the assessment to be understood.

Principle 2 **There must be a functional separation between Risk Assessment and Risk Management**

Risk Assessment of microbiological hazards is a scientific process aimed at identifying and characterising a microbiological hazard and estimating the risk of that hazard to a population. Risk management is a separate process aimed at identifying options for action(s) needed to manage that risk and has a policy function. Because risk assessment is objective, it is important that it is not influenced by Risk Management

Principle 3 **A structured approach must be used when conducting a Risk Assessment of Microbiological Hazards**

This structured approach must include four components: Hazard Identification, Hazard Characterisation, Exposure Assessment and Risk Characterisation. The sequence of use of these may vary depending on the purpose of the risk assessment.

Principle 4 **A Risk Assessment of Microbiological Hazards must clearly state both the purpose of the assessment and the form of the risk estimate that will be the output**

The scope of microbiological hazards associated with the specific food commodity need to be considered, together with an estimate of the likelihood of causing human illness. Any constraints need to be taken into consideration, such as proportion of raw: pasteurised egg used. The output might take the form of an estimate of the annual occurrence of illness. For example, the purpose might be to estimate the risk of contracting *Salmonella* food poisoning associated with consuming a product containing eggs.

Principle 5 Risk Assessment must be transparent

Risk Assessment will be transparent if the assessment is documented in full and a complete and formal record is made of the assessment enabling other risk assessors or staff to follow and agree the process. Any assumptions and judgements made during the assessment should be described and the rationale explained and fully documented in the record. The source of data used should be clearly recorded. The risk assessment and output drawn from it should be completely open to any audits or useful for any training subsequently carried out.

Principle 6 The risk estimate must contain a detailed description of uncertainty and where this arose during the risk assessment process

All risk assessments will contain a level of uncertainty which must be accountable. This must be quantified, fully described and recorded. There is less uncertainty associated with good quality data. If the uncertainty is assumed, the basis must be recorded. Uncertainty can sometimes be measured, in which case it must be quantified. It is important to note that uncertainty will always be associated with judgements made, assumptions drawn and data utilised.

Principle 7 Data must be of sufficient quality such that uncertainty in the risk estimate is minimised as far as possible

It is important that the best available information and expertise is applied to a risk assessment in order to reduce uncertainty and increase reliability of the risk estimate. Good quality data should be used wherever possible. When it is absent, the level of uncertainty associated with any output will be high. Preferably, quantitative information should be used where possible, but where this is not available, the best available qualitative information should be used.

Principle 8 A Risk Assessment of Microbiological Hazards must consider the interaction of the hazardous agent in the food with the process and the consumer

The dynamics of microbial growth, survival and death should be explicitly considered. Where applicable, the dynamics of microbial toxin formation and destruction could also be considered together with distribution of the agent, in appropriate foodstuffs. Assumptions may need to be made, such as the cell concentration at which toxins are produced. The interactions between humans and the agent (including possible sequelae) following consumption and the potential for horizontal or vertical spread of the agent are part of the assessment.

Principle 9 Risk estimates must be re-evaluated over time against human health data and when new data become available

There is a need to ensure that the risk assessment agrees with known experiences. If there are serious discrepancies, there must be a re-evaluation of the risk assessment. Regular review of the assessment is required in order to check the validity of assumptions, include any new information (e.g. is the hazard the same as it was?), and to keep the level of uncertainty as low as possible.

PART 2

GUIDE TO PERFORMING A MICROBIOLOGICAL RISK ASSESSMENT

SECTION 4 - INSTRUCTIONS FOR CARRYING OUT AN MRA

4.1 Introduction

This chapter outlines the considerations necessary to carry out a food industry MRA. The six formally recognised steps are: statement of purpose; hazard identification; exposure assessment; hazard characterisation; risk characterisation; and production of a formal report. These are broken down into component sub-steps. The additional step of performing an outline MRA is included here (Step 0). Not all of the sub-steps described here will be of relevance to every MRA carried out.

The process of carrying out the MRA has been set out here as various levels of complexity. It is important to note that there is no one method for carrying out an MRA. Consequently, published MRAs identified from the literature are used to illustrate possible approaches. It is important to note that these were not necessarily conducted as practical risk assessments, but published as part of studies into the development of risk assessment procedures. Discussion here is therefore not intended as a criticism of these but their consideration is useful in illustrating some components of the MRA process.

Where appropriate, commentary text is given for the relevant sub-steps by the authors of the papers. This illustrates the considerations required in each sub-step. Text is also quoted from the publications considered, to show how the authors have addressed the requirements.

4.2 Overview

Material in this section - that is, for carrying out a food industry MRA - is based on discussions described in Buchanan (1997), European Commission (1997), Hathaway (1997), Nickelson and Jakobsen (1997), Cassin *et al.* (1998) and CODEX (1998), which provide useful background sources.

The MRA route which produces the most accurate risk estimate, and therefore is the most desirable, is to provide a fully quantitative assessment with related uncertainties. This will often be very difficult due to lack of appropriate data, in which case semi-quantitative or qualitative methods can be used. Such techniques will not be as accurate as a full quantitative analysis.

Due to the complexity of the risk assessment process, only one hazard (or type of hazard e.g. infective pathogens) should be assessed at a time for a product. The risk assessment process must not be confused with the risk management process, by limiting its proposals or requirements to those that can currently be achieved in practice.

Significant specialist knowledge and time is required to conduct an MRA. Senior management need to be aware of this, and provide their full support if the outcome is to give a worthwhile assessment of risk.

MRA, like HACCP, requires multidisciplinary input, but may not require a formal meeting of the full team at every stage. The MRA will require a co-ordinator. Different resources and expertise may be called upon at different stages in the risk assessment process, individual inputs being drawn together at appropriate stages.

4.3 Step-by-Step Guide through an MRA

The step-by-step approach to conducting an MRA is mapped out in the form of a flow diagram in Figure 2. It is worth studying this for a while to become fully conversant with the standard structure and overall plan of approach to an MRA. This will provide a useful lead-in to the following sections which take each step, one at a time, for consideration in detail. These subsequent sections are presented in the following way:-

Step 0 — This is presented as an introductory description and a decision tree. These are designed to enable the user to establish, relatively quickly, whether a full risk assessment (carried out via Steps 1-6) is desirable and feasible.

Steps 1-6 — These are presented in a standard format which allows the process of MRA to be presented to a range of readers and allows for various levels of sophistication and complexity. It may not be appropriate or necessary for all readers to have an intimate knowledge of all the levels shown here. For this reason each of the Steps 1-6 is presented in a standard format to enable the user to identify the relevant parts in each step. The format is as follows:

Title of the step

A. This gives a general description of the step
B. This provides commentary text for each step, describing what is expected from someone carrying out an MRA. For clarity, each step is broken down into a series of numbered sub-steps. These need to be, at least, considered in carrying out the MRA.
C. This gives a technical description of the steps (again broken down into numbered sub-steps) in tabular form. The description is given in terms of Qualitative and Quantitative MRAs. These tables also give examples from published MRAs to illustrate the sub-steps where appropriate.

NB: *Technical terms used on these pages have specific meanings which need to be understood in order to use these pages effectively (see 1.6 Definition of Terms).*

Figure 2 - Risk Assessment Scheme for Foodborne Microbiological Hazards
Adapted from: Notermans, S., Mead, G.C. and Jouve, J.L. (1996)

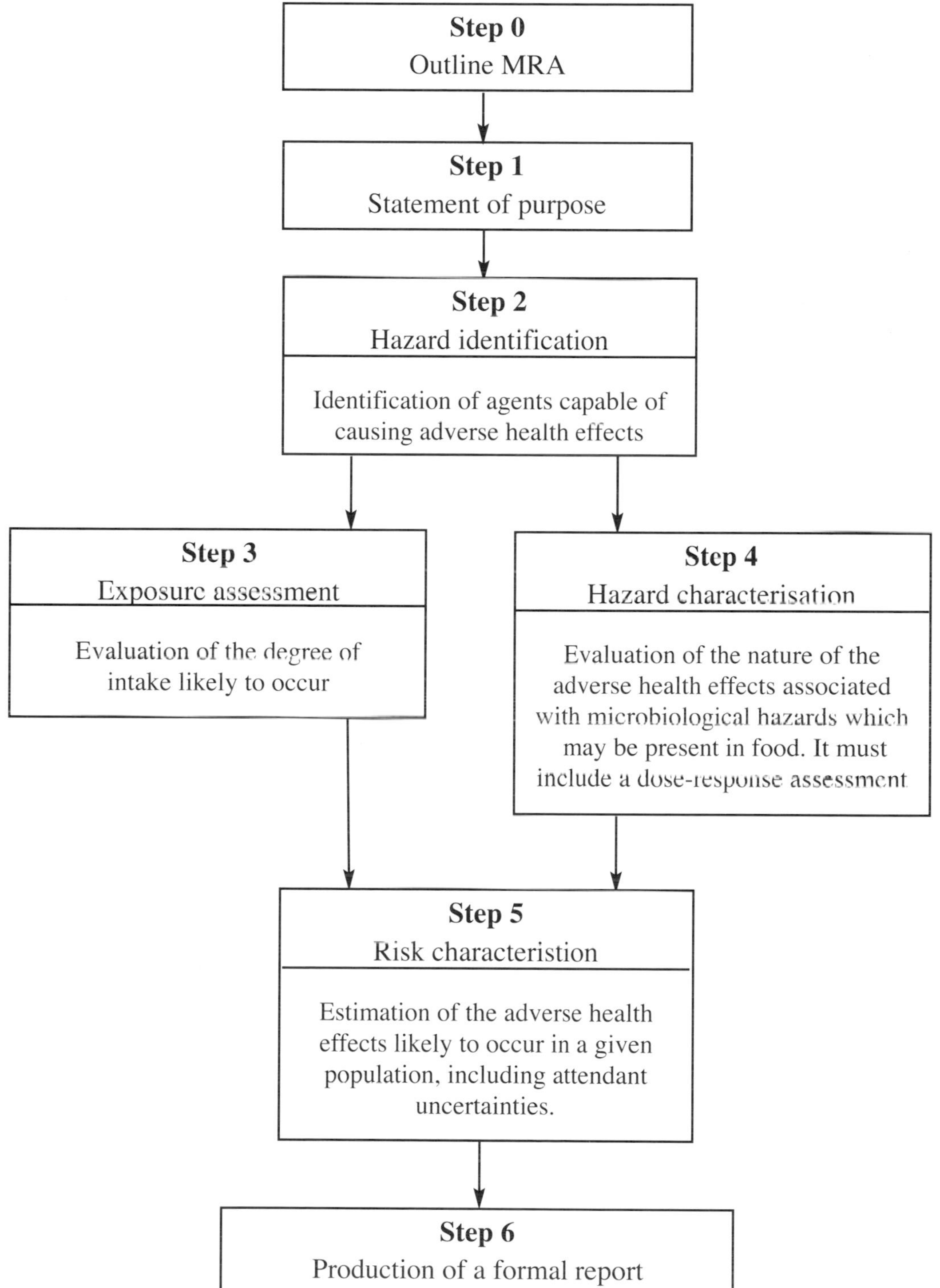

Step 0 - Outline MRA

In this step the specific purpose and scope of the risk assessment should be clearly stated. (This will be reiterated in Step 1.) The output form and possible output alternatives should also be defined.

Before the formal in-depth MRA can be carried out, an outline MRA (such as a Risk Profile described in Appendix 2 of this document) should be performed. This should be carried out by only one or possibly two people. In this process, consideration is given as to whether or not it is necessary to carry out a formal MRA. Thought processes for this are illustrated in the "decision tree" (Figure 3).

Carrying out this 'outline MRA' and producing a rough risk estimate is an important means for obtaining management commitment and assembling the team to go on to carry out the formal MRA.

The outline MRA will help to define the operational requirements in terms of time and resources needed for conducting an MRA. It may also highlight knowledge and data gaps relating to the MRA.

The task of obtaining Management commitment is worthy of separate consideration.

Management commitment

It is essential that senior management are fully briefed on the implications with regard to personnel time and other costs involved in conducting an MRA. Also, they must be fully committed to making resources available, and generally supporting the exercise.
The key points to be covered in this briefing are:

- Release of key personnel to attend MRA meetings - it is useful to give an estimate of number, frequency and duration of such meetings at this stage and make it clear that this estimate could vary as the MRA progresses

- The allocation of a suitable meeting room for the team as required.

- A budget to cover access to external expertise or information sources. This might involve the costs incurred in bringing an external expert to some meetings, or visiting an external source; or commissioning laboratory work (internal or external).

Figure 3 - Decision Tree for Outline Microbiological Risk Assessment

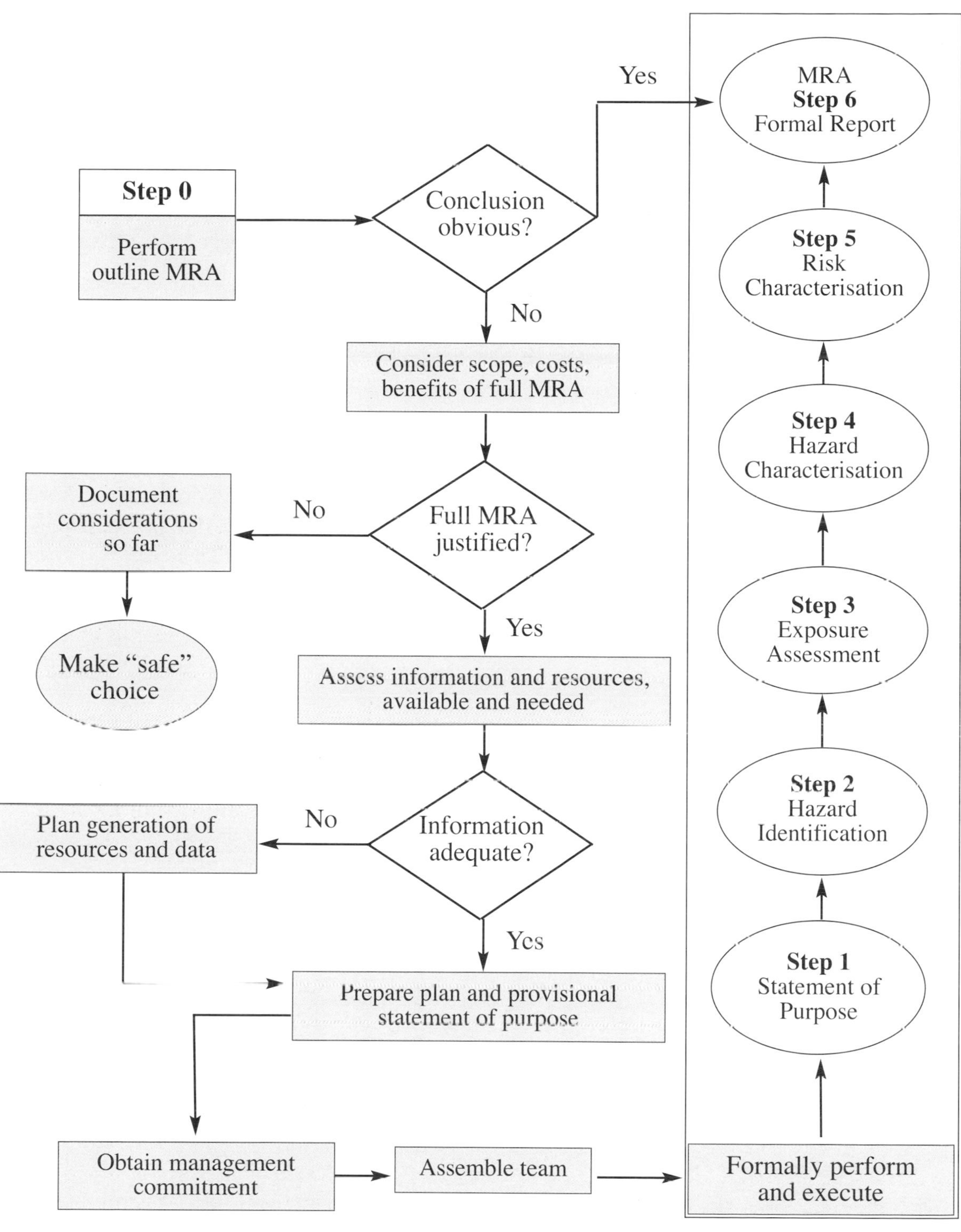

Step 1 - Statement of Purpose

The specific purpose and scope of the risk assessment should be clearly stated. The output form and possible output alternatives should be defined at the beginning.

A. Description

There are certain organisational issues to be considered within a business when carrying out an MRA. Before these issues can be addressed in detail, a decision on what to do needs to be made.

The first part of the process is to define the reason (the operational requirements) for carrying out the MRA. This can be done in terms of: scope; objective; expected output; form of output; nature of output; and date and by whom is it to be reviewed.

The second part is to clearly state the specific purpose of carrying out the exercise. This should be a disciplined procedure that clearly defines the food type, pathogen and required output.

B. Commentary text

Sub-step 1.1 - Scope

It is important that the scope of the MRA is clearly established at the beginning to focus the team's inputs and avoid generalised (generic) outputs.

The scope should clearly state:

- Pathogen of concern; food type/formulation and use; process; manufacturing site/line; and distribution (e.g. *Salmonella* in food type x, process y, plant z, chill-chain distribution) and any other factor likely to be of interest.

- Consumers using the product, and what their degree of susceptibility to the hazard is.

Each circumstance to be covered by a separate MRA, for example, if a different pathogen or different process is to be considered

Sub-step 1.2 - Objective(s)

The objective of the MRA should be agreed by the team. This will generally take the form of an objective to carry out an MRA (quantitative or qualitative) within the agreed scope and to an agreed timetable and output.

Sub-steps 1.3/1.4 - Expected form of output

This defines the format of the MRA output or conclusion and is usually defined by the company's Food Safety Requirements, which in turn might be influenced by regulatory Food Safety Objectives (FSO; e.g. *Salmonella* not detected in a product when examined to a stated sample plan and method).

A company Food Safety Requirement should tend to be more strict than a regulatory FSO, [i.e. variability of results means that commercial organisations need to be safely within their requirement to consistently meet them, and thereby minimise the level of failure.]

Outputs can be stated as:

- An estimate of the prevalence of illness, or
- An estimate of annual rate (e.g. incidence of illness per 100,000 population), or
- An estimate of the rate of illness and severity per eating occurrence.

Sub-step 1.5 - Date/who to review

Any MRA that is produced only continues to be useful if it is reviewed. A review will be prompted by new information becoming available (e.g. epidemiology, customer complaints, pathogen growth/death kinetics, change of process) and should be carried out by the re-assembly of the MRA team. If a review is not prompted by change of circumstances the team should review the MRA annually.

Sub-step 1.6 - Expertise/personnel/skills (The team)

The MRA team should comprise individuals providing the following skills and expertise:

- An individual with knowledge of the MRA procedure to act as team leader. He/she will fill the role of co-ordination and be responsible for guiding the exercise to the agreed output. The team leader must have an appreciation of handling uncertainty where definitive information is not available.

- An individual familiar with the manufacturing process/supply chain involved. It is important that they bring not only information on the 'standard process' to the assessment but also on any variations that might occur (e.g. re-worked materials, variations on overnight or weekend shifts, emergency procedures in the event of equipment breakdown).

- A microbiologist familiar with the microbiology of the food type and process under consideration. This input should extend to knowledge of variation in raw material microbiology; the effect of product formulation and process on relevant microorganisms; and shelf life potential in the designated market.

- A statistician familiar with protocols to estimate uncertainty where data is suspect or not available.

- An individual familiar with the market place to advise on likely consumer groups (e.g. healthy adults, immuno-compromised individuals or infants).

- An information scientist to obtain (from outside sources if necessary) and marshal information relevant to the MRA.

Sub-step 1.7 - Information sources

These include:

- Food Research Associations
- Food Standards Agency
- Food Research Institutes
- PHLS (Public Health Laboratory Service)
- Other consultants.

Sub-step 1.8 - Data sources

Information on the growth and/or death kinetics of target microorganisms under the conditions of the investigation (product formulation, processing conditions) is necessary in completing a quantitative MRA. It must be recognised that there is usually an interaction between formulation (e.g. pH, a_w, fat levels, structure, preservatives) and growth or process lethality so it might be impossible to reach definitive conclusions. Uncertainty can be reduced by:

- Getting better data
- Seeking expert external advice
- Commissioning challenge/shelf life experimental evaluations

Sub-step 1.9 - Resources required

Those required to gather, provide or supply information and/or data. Include items where expenditure is needed or has to be authorised.

C. Illustration of information required and used for MRA

The following landscape tables provide an illustration of the information required and used for qualitative and quantitative risk assessments, with reference to two published examples. It is important to appreciate that the published examples used were not necessarily conducted as practical risk assessments, but published as part of studies into the development of MRA procedures. This means that some of the cells in the table are blank as some issues will not have been included in these published MRAs. Also, the comments presented, therefore, are not intended as criticism but to help highlight the benefits and limitations of particular approaches.

Table 1 - Illustration of information required and used for qualitative and quantitative risk assessments (MRA), with published examples

STEP 1 - Statement of Purpose	**Type of Risk Assessment**		
	Qualitative Risk Assessment and Comparative Risk Assessment	**Quantitative Risk Assessment**	**Examples of published MRAs:**
	Should define the scope (1.1): specified hazards, materials, process, product and market and the objectives (1.2) to provide a risk assessment suitable for a specific audience using defined resources and (1.5) propose a date of review. These activities will not depend on the type of risk assessment, only the extent or detail will change. A comparative risk assessment will indicate whether a product (or process) is more or less risky than the nominated benchmark product (or process). **Example of a Statement of Purpose:** This MRA estimates the risk *or comparative risk* of food-poisoning from (a hazard) in (a product *or compared with a specified product*); the MRA includes the following factors (microbial lethality, growth or toxigenisis) and is valid for (consumers) when the specified supply chain *or change in the supply chain* is used.		**Example 1**. *Salmonella* in poultry. Brown *et al.*, 1998. **Example 2**. *E coli* O157 in beef hamburgers. Cassin *et al.*, 1998
1.1 Scope			**Example 1** "This Quantitative Risk Assessment estimates the risk of salmonellosis due to consumption of undercooked chicken." "From a processing point of view, the assessment concentrates on a single factor, the heating stage, controlled during manufacturing or by the customer, rather than on the sequence of production stages." **Example 2** "The prominence of *E coli* O157:H7 warrants the conduct of a detailed MRA to support management actions in both regulatory and HACCP programs"

	Qualitative Risk Assessment and Comparative Risk Assessment	**Quantitative Risk Assessment**	**Examples of published MRAs:**
1.2 Objective(s)			**Example 1** This study had two purposes: firstly, to use existing mathematical models to provide an MRA tool within the framework and definitions proposed for risk analysis and assessment by Codex, and secondly to provide a transparent, model-based MRA which would allow effective risk communication within a food manufacturing business. **Example 2** "This paper uses the term 'Process Risk Model' (PRM) which describes the integration and application of MRA methodology with scenario analysis and predictive microbiology to provide an objective assessment of the hygienic characteristics of a manufacturing process."
1.3 Expected outputs - a formal report understandable to the audience	The report must include a decision on safe or unsafe for specified hazards plus a rough estimate of distance from the safety criteria used *or in comparison with an existing or established product*; e.g. the MRA assesses the safety of a product based on specific default values or *in comparison with an existing product.*	The report must include a numerical estimate of probability of harm to consumers or the risk of failure against specific, probably numerical, targets, such as process or formulation conditions and dose-responses for consumers; e.g. the MRA presents the probability of infection or toxigenisis per meal for a defined consumer.	**Example 1** "To summarise, the models compute the chances of infection occurring from a chicken portion (which may be contaminated with salmonellae), when it has been subjected to a specified heating process, and ingested by an individual who may be sensitive to the remaining microbial dose." **Example 2** Probability of HUS and mortality. "The efficacy of three mitigation strategies were evaluated by modifying the values of the predictive factors and comparing the new predicted risk"

	Qualitative Risk Assessment and Comparative Risk Assessment	**Quantitative Risk Assessment**	**Examples of published MRAs:**
1.4 Form of output	Should outline a rough description of product safety borderline (safe or unsafe) and a summary of the information used. *For a comparative risk assessment it should outline the key product and process parameters providing safety.* E.g., based on the following information and assumptions the product is safe, for (X) factor it is on the borderline. *Or it is more/less safe than the existing product*	A statement of whether the product as designed is acceptable for sale/consumption or not. This statement will include a quantified expression of acceptable risks, e.g. 1 hazardous portion/10 million portions, and the dose response or types(s) of consumers to which the conclusion is limited. E.g. the risk estimate is (x) people infected/million portions processed and used in this way.	**Example 1** Risk estimate : Number of people infected per million portions sold. Graphical representation : % of people infected as a function of the lethality achieved during heating. **Example 2** Probability of haemolytic uraemic syndrome (HUS) or mortality per meal.
1.5 Date/Who to review	• reviewed when new information becomes available or at least annually • reviewed by expert team / factory management	• reviewed when new information becomes available or at least annually • reviewed by expert team / factory management	
1.6 Team expertise	**Minimum** - The team must be able to follow the elements of the risk assessment and produce a risk characterisation, recognising variability and identifying uncertainties. It may include the company microbiologist or QA manager and those responsible for control of key safety features and experts with relevant microbiological knowledge (food and public health) - especially on hazards and their control or elimination.	**Minimum** - The team must be able to produce a complete, quantified risk characterisation. It should include the company microbiologist or QA manager and those responsible for control of key safety features and experts with quantitative knowledge on food and public health microbiology, process conditions, product formulation and consumer sensitivity, exposure assessment and hazard characterisation. The team should also include the mathematical and statistical skills needed to specify the type of data needed and its format and for the assessment of probabilities.	**Example 1** Microbiologists and statisticians, not detailed in the paper **Example 2** Not stated but one assumes the authors plus those given in the acknowledgements section

	Qualitative Risk Assessment and Comparative Risk Assessment	Quantitative Risk Assessment	Examples of published MRAs:
1.7 and 1.8 Information and data sources	Company development and marketing records and experimental data, experts, recognised centres of expertise, industry and regulatory guides, specialist textbooks and articles on microbiology, food processing, epidemiology and consumer habits in similar circumstances. Consumer use and storage instructions.	Company development and marketing records or experimental data, experts and recognised centres of expertise with directly applicable data and information on processing and formulation, including predictive models which can provide quantitative information for analysis and decision making. Consumer use and storage instructions and data on usage habits.	*Data Sources* **Example 1** "All the data used in this Quantitative Risk Assessment comes from published scientific or internal unpublished surveys and are the most reliable available to the authors." **Example 2** These are given throughout the text and included in the references section
1.9 Resources required	Development personnel and company specialists, e.g. microbiologist or QA manager and external consultants or experts, e.g. Food RAs or RIs	Development personnel and company specialists, e.g. microbiologist, QA manager and statistician, and external consultants or experts, e.g. Food RA or RI with direct experience in the area	

Step 2 - Hazard Identification

"Hazard identification" identifies the microorganism or microbial toxin of concern and evaluates whether the microorganism or the toxin is a hazard when present in food.

A. Description

The outcome of this step in the process is a list of hazards. Specific expert knowledge will be needed to define which hazards are appropriate in a given circumstance (eg food and use). The name of the expert(s) needs to be recorded, together with the relevant data drawn upon to make decisions. The expert(s) must have access to all relevant data for this activity. The whole of this process should be expert led rather than process driven.

The hazard may already be known or defined, in which case these facts and the basis for how this knowledge was arrived at needs to be recorded. If not, either experts need to be consulted, or sources of information need to be assembled by experts. Wherever possible, consensus from more than one expert should be obtained before the MRA is started. In many cases, the experts and consensus can be obtained from expert centres such as Food Research Association's, Institute of Food Research, Trade Associations, Universities and so on.

B. Commentary text

Sub-step 2.1 - List of hazards

The output from this step will be a list of hazards; the hazards may already be known or well-defined, e.g. *Cl. botulinum* in low acid canned foods, *S.* Enteritidis in eggs, *E. coli* O157 in beefburgers and *B. cereus* in rice, in which case these facts and how this knowledge was arrived at must be recorded. Certain hazards may be associated with different food groups, e.g. *L. monocytogenes* in chilled foods.

Sub-step 2.2 - Name of expert(s)

If the hazards are not clear or are unknown, advice must be sought from the appropriate experts. This is particularly the case when considering so-called emerging pathogens. If possible, opinion should be obtained from more than one expert.

Access to experts can usually be obtained through technical centres, Food Research Associations, Institute for Food Research, trade associations, universities, etc.

It is important that experts have a significant amount of experience in microbiological issues and have a relevant amount of scientific knowledge. A failure to correctly identify a hazard could potentially render the risk assessment ineffective, with the resultant hazards remaining in the product or process.

Sub-step 2.3 - Relevant data/facts and basis recorded (justification)

The (microbiology) expert will need access to relevant information such as clinical studies, epidemiological studies and surveillance, characteristics and properties of microorganisms and the effect of the food-chain on the microorganism, in order to determine the relevance of different microorganisms and their toxins to a particular food.

Sub-step 2.4 - Sources of information consulted

All relevant data and facts must be recorded, including the basis for any decisions, i.e. the justification for the identification of the hazard or hazards.

It could be considered that the hazard identification step is so distinct, and often will require access to a range of experts, that it would be performed outside the MRA team. In this case, it is vital that all details surrounding decisions are fully documented so that the team fully understand the reasoning behind the hazard identification.

C. Illustration of information required and used for MRA

The following landscape tables provide an illustration of the information required and used for qualitative and quantitative risk assessments, with reference to two published examples. It is important to appreciate that the published examples used were not necessarily conducted as practical risk assessments, but published as part of studies into the development of MRA procedures. This means that some of the cells in the table are blank as some issues will not have been included in these published MRAs. Also, the comments presented, therefore, are not intended as criticism but to help highlight the benefits and limitations of particular approaches.

Table 2 - Illustration of information required and used for qualitative and quantitative risk assessments (MRA), with published examples

STEP 2 - Hazard Identification	**Type of Risk Assessment**		**Examples of published MRAs:**
	Qualitative Risk Assessment and Comparative Risk Assessment	**Quantitative Risk Assessment**	
	(2.1) The hazards considered e.g. types of micro-organism or toxins (defined by the producer micro-organism) must always be stated. (2.2) The experts or other personnel and the knowledge/ skills they contribute to the study must be recorded. (2.3) All the information and data used by the study must be recorded and information discarded after examination should also be noted, with reasons. *Where a comparative risk assessment is being done, this information concerning the 'benchmark' product should be assembled in addition to information on the 'new' product, so that the basis of its safety is understood.* (2.4) Any additional resources that would improve the quality of the output, with an estimate of the cost/benefit and likely timing, should be noted.		**Example 1**. *Salmonella* in poultry. Brown *et al*., 1998. **Example 2**. *E coli* O157 in beef hamburgers. Cassin *et al*., 1998
2.1 List of hazard(s)			**Example 1** *Salmonella* : "Salmonellosis from poultry, and especially chicken meat, has been identified as a major type of human food-poisoning" **Example 2** "The methodology was applied to model the human health risk associated with *Escherichia coli* O157:H7 in ground beef hamburgers." "The hazard associated with the consumption of hamburgers in this risk assessment was *Escherichia coli* O157:H7."
2.2 Name of expert(s)			**Example 1** See reference in Hazard identification : • Bryan, F. L. and M. P. Doyle (1995) Health risks and consequences of *Salmonella* and *Campylobacter jejuni* in raw poultry. J. Food Prot. **58**:326-344.

	Qualitative Risk Assessment and Comparative Risk Assessment	Quantitative Risk Assessment	Examples of published MRAs:
2.2 Name of expert(s) (continued)			• Mead, G. C. (1982). Microbiology of poultry and game birds. pp. 67-101. In M. H. Brown (Ed.). Meat Microbiology. Applied Science Publ. Ltd., London. • Todd, E. C. D. (1978). Foodborne disease in six countries - a comparison. J. Food Prot. **41**:559-565. **Example 2** References given in section 3
2.3 Relevant data/ facts and basis recorded (Justification)			**Example 1** Chickens carry salmonellae in their intestines and on and in their skin, therefore poultry meat is frequently contaminated. The consumption of salmonellae with apparently cooked poultry products is a potential public health problem, because poultry meat can appear cooked before it is pasteurised and hence may contain infective cells. (See reference above for sources). **Example 2** "It has been shown that cattle may be a reservoir of *E coli* O157:H7, and that contamination of carcasses during slaughter and processing may be the manner by which beef and beef products become contaminated and transmit the organism to humans. Well documented clinical findings link *E coli* O157:H7 to human health effects, and the probability that *E coli* O157:H7 presents a hazard to humans is assumed to be 100%." "Undercooked or raw ground beef has been frequently implicated in foodborne outbreaks."
2.4. Sources of information consulted			

Step 3 - Exposure Assessment

The ultimate goal of exposure assessment is to evaluate the level of microorganisms or microbial toxins in the food at the time of consumption. This may include an assessment of actual or anticipated human exposure due to consumption

A. Description

The exposure assessment will be contamination led (based on identified hazards and their context); changes that occur throughout the manufacturing process will need to be considered, as will what is taken in at the point of consumption. If this data is not to hand, there is a need to acquire it. This may be done in a structured way with the help of a flow diagram. Variability and uncertainty need to be recorded.

Assessing the potential extent of food contamination involves consideration of the frequency or likelihood of contamination of foods by the pathogenic agent and its prevalence and/or level in the foods over time, up to the time of consumption.

In addition to the characteristics of the pathogen, information of interest may include:-

- The microbial ecology of the food.
- The initial contamination of the raw materials.
- The effect of the production, processing, handling and distribution steps, and preparation by the final consumer on the microbial agent (i.e. the impact of each step on the level of the pathogenic agent of concern).
- The variability in processes involved and the level of process control.
- The level of sanitation.
- The potential for (re)contamination (e.g. cross contamination from other foods; recontamination after a killing treatment).
- The methods or conditions of packaging, distribution and storage of the food (e.g. temperature of storage, relative humidity of the environment, gaseous composition of the atmosphere).
- The characteristics of the food that may influence the potential for growth of the pathogen (and/or toxin production) in the food under various conditions, including abuse (e.g. pH, moisture content or water activity, nutrient content, presence of anti-microbial substances, competitive flora).
- Usage instructions, e.g storage, cooking.

To gain this information, several techniques may be used, for example:-

- Data collection on prevalence and distribution of microorganisms in food(s) including foods involved in outbreaks.
- Storage testing.
- Challenge testing.
- Historical performance data of food process or laboratory studies of such performance (e.g. 'D' values of survivors of a heat treatment).
- Mathematical modelling to predict the growth, death or survival of microorganisms in response to environmental conditions and the likely number of microorganisms present in food at the time of consumption.
- Examination of foods involved in outbreaks.

Such exposure assessment includes various levels of uncertainty. This uncertainty can be estimated using various techniques, e.g. event tree analysis, fault tree analysis, HAZOP (Hazard Analysis and Operability Study) and probabilistic scenario analysis (PSA) (see USDA, 1997; DH, 1997).

Information on consumption patterns and habits ("dietary information") may include:-

- Socio-economic and cultural background, ethnicity.
- Consumer preferences and behaviour as they influence the choice and the amount of food intake (e.g. frequent consumption of high risk foods).
- Average serving size and distribution of sizes.
- Amount of food consumed over a year considering seasonality and regional differences.
- Food preparation practices (e.g. cooking habits and/or cooking time, temperature used, extent of home storage and conditions, including abuse).
- Demographics and size of exposed population(s) (e.g. age distribution, susceptible groups).

The following skills are required

- Someone familiar with the processing activities.
- Company microbiologist.
- Someone with numeric skills, e.g. statistician.
- Someone familiar with the marketplace
- Information scientist.

One or more of these skills could be represented by a consultant.

If the skills are difficult to obtain, the 'team leader' must have an appreciation of handling uncertainty - to the extent that decisions to fail-safe rather than fail-dangerous, or not to go on, can be made.

B. Commentary text

Sub-step 3.1 - Sources of contamination

Assessing the potential extent of food contamination involves consideration of the frequency or likelihood of contamination of foods by the pathogenic agent and its prevalence and/or level in the foods over time, up to the time of consumption. There are a number of reasons why foods may be contaminated with pathogenic microorganisms. These vary from: production of foods using poor quality raw ingredients, through inadequate or inappropriate processing of the food, to contamination of the food post-manufacture. Handling of the food by the consumer can be a source of contamination including cross-contamination routes.

Sub-step 3.2 - Changes through manufacture (growth/survival/death)

To reduce the chances of occurrence of a pathogen in the finished food, the quality of the raw ingredients used needs to be as high as possible. Should the pathogen of concern in the risk assessment be present at this stage, the features of any processing that the raw ingredients go through to produce the product is of great importance in determining the extent of risk associated with that pathogen. This needs to be considered at three levels:

- Is the pathogen going to grow if present in the foodstuff at any stage in the process (e.g. manufacture, preparation, distribution, sale)?
- Is it going to survive any processing, including treatment of the food by the ultimate purchaser/consumer of the food?
- Will the pathogen be destroyed in the preparation of the food, e.g. cooked/baked by the consumer prior to consumption?

Sub-step 3.3 - Level of hazard in kind of food

The number of hazardous microorganisms present in the foodstuff throughout its manufacture to time of consumption needs to be determined, because the more microorganisms present, the greater the risk that a pathogen is consumed. This will lead to an increased risk of illness through consumption of the foodstuff. The level of hazard throughout the manufacture of the food may vary; however, the level at point of consumption is of greatest importance.

Sub-step 3.4 - Flow diagram/describe the system

In order to determine where the points of most concern are likely to be in the processing of a foodstuff, the process needs to be described adequately. This is best done in a way that all of the MRA 'team' can understand. A flow diagram of the process can be very useful for this purpose. The flow diagram can be based on one already produced for a HACCP study, for example; however, aspects such as the potential for (re)contamination (e.g. cross contamination from other foods; recontamination after a killing treatment) need to be considered.

Sub-step 3.5 - Variability in the system

Taking an 'average' view of how an 'average' consumer may behave may conceal variability in likely exposure to the pathogen. For example, if a food can be consumed cold, or after reheating by the purchaser, there may be a different exposure level for different consumers. Variability should be explicitly considered, and reported if it is substantial.

Sub-step 3.6 - Uncertainty

The estimated exposure and variability are unlikely to be the exact, true values. It is important to indicate the range of values that might reasonably be expected to include the true values. That range may be summarised as ± figures on the estimates, but the report should make clear how uncertainty was estimated.

Sub-step 3.7 - Qualitative characterisation

Ideally the exposure assessment should be described in numerical terms, i.e. quantitatively. To be able to do this, a large amount of resource is required in terms of the quality of data and time. For a food manufacturer, it is likely that this type of determination is not possible, consequently a 'ranking' or qualitative system may be used. Such a system may give categories of 'high', 'medium' or 'low' exposure.

If this approach is taken, it is important to state what the categorisation is based upon.

Sub-step 3.8 - Predictive microbiology

The following are important uses of predictive microbiology, a tool which can be used to gain relevant data on the effects of:

- the methods or conditions of packaging,
- distribution and storage of the food (e.g. temperature of storage, relative humidity of the environment, gaseous composition of the atmosphere); and
- the characteristics of the food that may influence the potential for growth of the pathogen (and/or toxin production) in the food under various conditions, including abuse (e.g. pH, moisture content or water activity, nutrient content, presence of anti-microbial substances, competitive flora).

To gain the information which will be of use in carrying out the exposure assessment, several techniques may be used. These can be divided (in broad terms) into:

practical: data collection on prevalence and distribution of microorganisms in food(s) including foods involved in outbreaks; storage testing; challenge testing; historical performance data of food process or laboratory studies of such performance (e.g. 'D' values of survivors of a heat treatment); and

theoretical: mathematical modelling to predict the likely growth, death or survival of microorganisms in response to environmental conditions and the likely number of microorganisms present in food at the time of consumption; and examination of foods involved in outbreaks.

Sub-step 3.9 - Patterns of consumption

Relevant information in 'exposure assessment' terms on consumption patterns and habits ("dietary information") may include: socio-economic and cultural background, ethnicity; consumer preferences and behaviour as they influence the choice and the amount of food intake (e.g. frequent consumption of high risk foods); average serving size and distribution of sizes, amount of food consumed over a year considering seasonality and regional differences; food preparation practices (e.g. cooking habits and/or cooking time, temperature used, extent of home storage and conditions, including abuse); and demographics and size of exposed population(s) (e.g. age distribution, susceptible groups).

Sub-step 3.10 - Resources required

The chief resource required is one of manpower, especially in terms of knowledge and expertise. The minimum skills needed to investigate this step are: someone familiar with the processing activities; company microbiologist; someone with numeric skills, e.g. statistician; someone familiar with the marketplace; and an information scientist (one or more of these skills could be represented by a consultant).

If the skills are difficult to obtain, the 'team leader' must have an appreciation of handling uncertainty - to the extent that decisions fail-safe rather than fail-dangerous.

C. Illustration of information required and used for MRA

The following landscape tables provide an illustration of the information required and used for qualitative and quantitative risk assessments, with reference to two published examples. It is important to appreciate that the published examples used were not necessarily conducted as practical risk assessments, but published as part of studies into the development of MRA procedures. The comments presented, therefore, are not intended as criticism but to help highlight the benefits and limitations of particular approaches.

Table 3 - Illustration of information required and used for qualitative and quantitative risk assessments (MRA), with published examples

STEP 3 - Exposure Assessment	**Type of Risk Assessment** **Qualitative Risk Assessment and Comparative Risk Assessment**	**Quantitative Risk Assessment**	**Examples of published MRAs:**
			Example 1. *Salmonella* in poultry. Brown *et al.*, 1998. **Example 2**. *E coli* O157 in beef hamburgers. Cassin *et al.*, 1998
3.1 Sources of contamination	The team must identify and describe **realistic** sources of contamination **covering the supply and use chain** and record the reasons for choice of contaminant. E.g Factory layout and simple descriptive flow diagram indicating typical or design conditions and realistic sources of contamination. *For a comparative risk assessment this should be done for the benchmark and the new product.*	The team must quantify the impact of various sources of contamination in the **supply and use chain** and present the information sources used with estimates of variability and uncertainty. E.g. Factory layout and descriptive flow diagram indicating running conditions and their range and realistic sources and levels of and changes in levels of contamination.	**Example 1** Raw material (Chicken meat) "The incidence of infectious agent in the poultry raw material. This is the likelihood of the raw material being contaminated with salmonellae. For poultry in the UK this is typically 33%. Data on variability of incidence is not readily available, but the impact of higher or lower values can be tested. Level and distribution of microorganisms in the raw material. The lognormal distribution has been used to describe the distribution of Enterobacteriaceae found in meat comminutes, and may also be used to describe the distribution of salmonellae. Published data on *Salmonella* generally gives the prevalence of the microbe (i.e. percentage of samples positive), not its numbers or a statistical description of their variability."
3.1 Sources of contamination (continued)			**Example 2** "Faecal material"; "feeding practices have been shown to affect the growth of the pathogen"; "the increase in prevalence was based on the possibility of cross-contamination before and during the dressing procedure"

	Qualitative Risk Assessment and Comparative Risk Assessment	Quantitative Risk Assessment	Examples of published MRAs:
3.2 Changes through manufacture	The likely presence or levels of the hazard in raw materials should be based on specifications, storage conditions and the effect of processing and use on numbers (increase or decrease) or toxin production. Changes should be estimated for each process and use stage. All assumptions must be clearly stated with accompanying reasoning. *A comparative risk assessment should cover the benchmark and new products and clearly identify any changes and their consequences or increasing or decreasing risk.* For infectious pathogens, unless data on consumer sensitivity is available, the assumption should be that 1 cell/portion may be infectious and survival is a hazard. As a general rule where numbers of toxin-producers exceed 100,000/g then the presence of toxin is a possibility. If the food properties are unknown (i.e. pH, A_W and temperatures) then toxigenisis at these levels of micro-organisms should be assumed. E.g. Raw materials containing less than 10^2 *Salmonella*/g were used, the maximum process duration was <8h at <12°C (no growth) and the factory cooking reached 70°C internal temperature (> 4 log reductions) and sealed packaging was used (no re-contamination) and the customer cooking instructions were 70°C x 2 mins (>6 log reduction).	The likely numbers in raw materials should be based on specifications and storage conditions. The effect of processing, storage and use on numbers (increase or decrease) and toxin production must be known/determined for each process and use stage. All assumptions must be clearly stated with accompanying reasoning. Data or models for the growth or survival of infectious pathogens and toxigenisis and toxin degradation should be used to describe the impact of processing, product composition and eating habits on the likely concentration and persistence of the hazardous agent. For example a process stage (x_7) may induce stress-related increased heat resistance and fat enrobement protect any ingested organisms For infectious pathogens, data on consumer sensitivity should be available and survival should be considered a hazard. Whether toxigenisis is realistic in the in-process material, residual material or the product (i.e. based on nutrients, pH, A_W and temperature) must be determined. As a general rule, where numbers of toxin-producers exceed 100,000/g then toxin production is a possibility. E.g. there was a 1 log increase at stage x, where toxigenisis could occur and a further 2 log increase (stages x_1 - x_2)outside the boundaries of toxigenisis.	**Example 1** "The QRA is only complete when the reduction in numbers caused by cooking and therefore the remaining dose is taken into account. In this example the product has been kept frozen, and therefore the numbers entering the heat process are assumed to be the same as in the raw material. Thus this case study only considers the effect of heating. The calculated process lethality is based on the temperature and time at each point of the product (computed from a heat transfer model)... A simple log-linear (D and z-value) model based on published values was used to represent the fate of salmonellae during a heat treatment. It is assumed that the kinetics of inactivation in these frozen products are not significantly different from the published values and it is also assumed that any survivors are infectious, though this may result in a conservative model. The heating time in seconds for a decimal reduction of microbes at temperature T°C is estimated by : $D=10^{\left[\frac{83.4-T}{10.4}\right]}$ " **Example 2** This is covered in sections *3.2.3.1 Microbial growth* and *3.2.3.2 Thermal inactivation* of the paper. Growth is considered "between time of production and the time of consumption." The effect of different cooking procedures is considered.

	Qualitative Risk Assessment and Comparative Risk Assessment	Quantitative Risk Assessment	Examples of published MRAs:
3.3 Level or hazard in a unit of food	Where the hazard is realistic or has not been eliminated, the chances of an infectious or toxigenic dose for the target consumers must be assessed using process, storage and formulation data. E.g. *Salmonella* may be present in 10% of portions at an infectious level. *For a comparative risk assessment this information should be collected for the benchmark and the new product, so that a comparison can be done and any increase or decrease in risk indicated.*	The numbers or probability of micro-organisms or toxin being present at the point of consumption must be assessed using the growth/survival/death/toxigenesis kinetics associated with the food and its use. E.g. the mean number of *Salmonella* per portion will be (log2.0) i.e. 100/g with a variability of (SD) +/- (log 1.0).	**Example 1** Result of the exposure assessment but already integrated in the risk equation. Function of the size of the portion, the initial contamination of the raw material and the log-kill achieved by the heat treatments. **Example 2** This is covered in *3.2.4 Consumption.* "The ingested dose is a function of the concentration of the organism in the beef at the time of consumption..."
3.4 Description of the supply and use chain **3.5 Variability**	Flow diagram of the supply and use chain for the proposed product *(and for a comparative risk assessment for the benchmark product)* should include the design temperatures and times and their likely variability indicated and used as limits for the exposure assessment (EA). E.g. stages x_1 - x_6 <12°C, x_7 = 70°C x 2 mins, x_8 <10°C within 3h, distribution <7°C, home shelf-life 1 week @ 10°C. Variability should be estimated.	Flow diagram of the supply and use chain with the design temperatures and times and their variability indicated from measured attributable data which should be in sufficient detail to allow kinetic models to be used. E.g. stages x_1 - x_6 12°C +/- 2.5°C; time 2 - 7h, x_7 = 70+/- 0.5°C x 2 +/- 0.1 mins, x_8 90% of packs <10°C within 3h, 100% within 5h, distribution <7+/-2°C, home shelf-life 1 week +/- 5d @ 2 - 12°C.	**Example 1** Raw material contamination : Uses a Log-Normal distribution to model variability of contamination **Example 2** Variability and uncertainty are covered in section *4.3 Importance analysis.* "The Beta-binomial model yields variability for probability of illness for a particular dose" Monte Carlo simulation was used to assess the effect of uncertainty and variability in the model parameters on the predicted human health risk.

	Qualitative Risk Assessment and Comparative Risk Assessment	Quantitative Risk Assessment	Examples of published MRAs:
3.6 Uncertainty	A description of the major sources of uncertainty should be associated with the description of the supply and use chain. This type of assessment can be more or less useless - for example, if the product is safe with a high uncertainty. *A comparative risk assessment cannot be done if there is high uncertainty associated with the benchmark product- the determinants of safety must be known.* E.g. conditions at the process stages are not known, but assumed to provide specified acceptable conditions	Sources of uncertainty should be clearly identified and their impact on the risk estimate quantified.	**Example 1** Not available but mentioned : "However, users need to be aware that any 'answers' from the QRA will only be as good as the data used and they should identify and evaluate the importance of errors associated with a prediction." **Example 2** Variability and uncertainty are covered in section 4.3 *Importance analysis.* Monte Carlo simulation was used to assess the effect of uncertainty and variability in the model parameters on the predicted human health risk. See Fig 2 for plot of 'average probability of illness' against 'ingested dose' with uncertainty.
3.7 Qualitative characterisation and 3.8 predictive microbiology	A qualitative characterisation of the risks is produced and the benefits of predictive micro-biology will be limited by the quality of other process and product information. The range of sensitivity of consumers should be considered and the characterisation should be based on the most sensitive likely to consume product. E.g. the predictions on process lethality used were based on laboratory studies against *Salmonella. If the comparative risk assessment is done to examine the impact of a change in marketing strategy, e.g. targeting children by advertising - which will alter the consumer mix, then this must be reflected in the characteri-sation of the most sensitive consumers.*	A quantitative description of risks will be produced and predictive microbiology can be used in conjunction with process kinetics and a description of the product in microbiological and 'protective' terms to allow defined risk estimates. The basis of conclusions should be put in probabilistic terms. E.g. predictive models for growth had been validated for the food product.	Example 1 Use of a thermal inactivation model (D and z-value model) : $D=10^{\left[\frac{83.4-T}{10.4}\right]}$ " **Example 2** In this study the PRM incorporated 2 mathematical sub-models: The first described the behaviour of the pathogen from food production through processing, handling and consumption to predict human exposure. (Hygienic quality of the system).

	Qualitative Risk Assessment and Comparative Risk Assessment	Quantitative Risk Assessment	Examples of published MRAs:
3.7 and 3.8 (Continued)			*The exposure estimate was "inputted" to a dose-response model to estimate the health risk (rather than hygiene) associated with consuming food from the process. Risk to human health was regarded as the measure of the quality of the system.*
3.9 Patterns of consumption and use	Should be based on storage, use or portion-size instructions, unless there is data to suggest that other practices can significantly alter risk or dose, e.g. undercooking. Public health data may be used to increase knowledge of likely abuse conditions and risks. E.g. storage below 10°C, use within 3 days, portion size 50g, cook 5 minutes under medium heat.	Should be based on consumer data on storage and use, unless this data suggests that other practices occurring at a low frequency may increase risk (dose). Predictive modelling of microbial fate may be used to examine the impact of variation. E.g. range of storage conditions 5 - 20°C, 1 - 6d, portion 25 - 150g, typical product heating curves.	**Example 1** Some assumptions on consumer use : • "During home cooking it is assumed that heat is only supplied to one face at a time, and a single face is exposed to the heat source for 70% of the cook time and the opposite face for 30%, to simulate grilling or pan-frying." • For the risk calculation it is assumed that each consumer eats a whole portion of chicken and one only. **Example 2** This is covered in *3.2.4 Consumption* Considerations were: portion size and degree of cooking
3.10 Resources required for Exposure Assessment	Development personnel and company specialists e.g.microbiology, production, marketing, home economists or QA manager + external consultants or experts e.g. RA's, RI's or EHO's.	Development personnel and company specialists e.g. production, microbiologist, QA manager and statistician plus external consultants or experts e.g. market research, RA RI or EHO's with direct experience in the area	**Example 1** Epidemiological information, knowledge of food manufacturing processes; mathematical modelling skills.

Step 4 - Hazard Characterisation

Hazard characterisation is an assessment of the nature of the adverse health effects associated with a hazard which may be present in foods. Ideally this should be quantitative, but can be qualitative. Where possible, a dose-response assessment should be performed.

The purpose of hazard characterisation is to provide an estimate of the nature, severity and duration of the adverse effects associated with harmful agents in food. Factors important to consider relate to the microorganisms, the dynamics of infection and the sensitivity of the host.

A. Description

ICMSF (1998) utilise the 'case plan structure matrix' of severity of effect and the impact of product usage on risk. However, local institutions or companies can provide more specific information, e.g. national public health services. The key is to fail safe.

The selection and handling of dose-response curve(s) is of importance here. Dose-response assessment is the process of obtaining quantitative information on the probability of human illness following exposure to a hazard; it is a translation of exposure to harm.

There is a need to stress that the leader of this stage of the MRA needs to be able to handle data uncertainty, as the data used to generate the dose-response curve will have uncertainty associated with it.

B. Commentary text

Sub-step 4.1 - Adverse health effects (nature/severity/duration)

When an individual or a population consumes a food-poisoning agent (an infectious agent, e.g. *Salmonella,* or a pre-formed toxin, e.g. staphylococcal) the adverse health effects will depend on:

- The food-poisoning agent
- The individual consumer
- The food product
- The consumption pattern

Hazard characterisation uses this information to describe or quantify the nature of the adverse effects for the consumers described in the scope of the risk assessment.

Each hazardous agent will give rise to characteristic symptoms (illness) depending on the type of damage caused if they reach sensitive body tissues. The range of probabilities of causing illness and the severity of the effects may be wide within any population of consumers and severity will generally increase as the level of the agent in the product increases, although there may be a minimum threshold for toxigenesis.

Recognition of certain adverse effects or symptoms in individuals and defined populations is often used as the basis for deriving dose response relationships and these are typical for a specific agent and consumer. Some agents may exhibit a range of pathogenicities (virulence or toxicity), e.g. different types of *Salmonella* and *E. coli* or toxins from different types of clostridia, therefore the agent in question needs to be well characterised and at least specified in the scope. For a realistic hazard characterisation, it is important to obtain information on the main factors influencing pathogenicity - toxigenicity (the severity of the effects produced in the host by a certain dose) and invasiveness (the ability of the agent to invade or reach sensitive tissues in the host).

Sub-step 4.2 - Dose-response

The dose response describes the number of microorganisms or dose of toxin that will cause an adverse response (be it illness or death, for example) in an individual. Usually this type of risk assessment will deal with an acute exposure.

There may be different dose responses when different individuals or sub-populations are exposed to similar amounts or consumption or preparation patterns differ. If the agent is an infectious pathogen with a low minimum infectious dose, then portion size will be less important as the minimum dose may be exceeded in a few grams of product. However if a substantial dose is required for infection, or the agent is a toxin, then portion size and consumption pattern will be important in determining adverse effects. For a given population, variations are often summarised as a dose response curve showing the proportion of consumers affected at any given level of agent. These curves typically relate the chances of illness or the development of typical symptoms to the specified agent consumed at certain concentrations. Few curves representing typical consumers or taking account of different consumption patterns are available and those published do not show the distribution of severity of illness (infection or intoxication) within a population. However, they may be used to provide a broad indication of the effects of the agent and highlight differences in sensitivity between particular groups, such as healthy adults and children. Extrapolation to humans from animal models will provide information of only limited value.

Sub-step 4.3 - Different end points (e.g. sickness/death)

If consumers become ill, they may exhibit a range of symptoms and different severities of illness ranging from mild discomfort to hospitalisation or death. Illness may be transient, only affecting the victim for a day, week or month or it may lead to permanent harm. Where illness is caused by infection, it will often have a longer duration (>1 week) with a gradual onset, whereas illnesses caused by toxins will have a more rapid onset and may be over more quickly. A population of consumers can be described as susceptible to, infected with or recovered from a disease. Infection may also lead to carriers who are infectious, but do not exhibit symptoms or those who remain infectious after recovery. Identification of this state may be considered as part of the hazard characterisation.

Sub-step 4.4 - Ideally quantitative

Ideally there would be a numerically based hazard characterisation of the food-poisoning agent, the individual consumer, the food product and the consumption pattern. This would provide the best input to the risk characterisation, allowing transparent communication and direct comparisons to be made between studies with a minimum of interpretation or expert intervention.

A quantitative description would include:-

- Numbers or concentrations describing the prevalence of the agent, or the range of agents, at the point of consumption, and taking account of the pattern of consumption. For infectious pathogens, hazard characterisation should provide details of the species or types (e.g. for *Salmonella* or *E. coli* O157:H7) involved. For a pre-formed toxin, a description would be based on the species of the producing microorganism and any effects of the food, its processing, storage and usage on toxin levels and distribution.
- Individual consumers and populations of consumers would be described in terms of their sensitivity to the agent and the severity of symptoms. Such descriptions may be based on the major risk factors of age, sex or health status and should include any higher sensitivities relevant to sub-populations. This would allow valid comparisons to be made and the use of existing information.

Sub-step 4.5 - Can be qualitative (e.g. ranking system)

For the food producer this is likely to be the most accessible way of characterising the food poisoning agent, the individual consumer, food product and consumption pattern to provide a hazard characterisation. The output has to be sufficiently accurate (low variability and uncertainty) to provide a meaningful input to the risk characterisation. If sufficient information is available from this stage to make a reasonable decision regarding a particular risk, this should be communicated to the risk manager. Any assumptions or generalisations must be described and their likely impact on the output of the hazard characterisation must be noted. Where possible those assumptions (such as minimum infectious dose, published dose response data or the representation of customer abuse or cooking conditions and consumption patterns) exerting the most effect on the output of this stage of analysis should be the best described. Their identification and description may be a two-stage process, where initial assumptions are made and then refined, as more data becomes available, allowing the important factors to be identified with increased certainty.

The concentration of the agent in the food at the point of consumption may be described as high (e.g. above the hazardous level), medium (e.g. around the hazardous level) or low (e.g. below the hazardous level) and should be provided by the exposure assessment. As the level will be further modified by information on consumption patterns, a broad dose range may be the best detail available to work with, even though it may extend over several orders of magnitude. For infectious pathogens, hazard characterisation should at least provide details of the species or strain.

Sub-step 4.6 - Status of microorganism

Infectious pathogens - the origin or pre-treatment of many infectious pathogens during food processing and storage can influence their ability to cause illness. Generally any pathogens in a food will be dead (non-viable), surviving, or growing very slowly. If there is temperature abuse involving high temperature (in the growth range) storage or accidental re-contamination, then cells may be actively growing and therefore provide a higher dose when consumed. Significant treatments affecting infectivity include mild or sub lethal heating, freezing or chemical preservation (e.g. acid or reduced aw). Such factors relevant to the food in question and any assumptions based on them should be noted.

Toxigenic pathogens - to be harmful, toxigenic pathogens have to grow in the food or its raw materials under conditions where they can produce toxin in sufficient quantity to cause symptoms. Toxins may be pre-formed in food, but they may also be produced by some species of microorganisms in the gut after consumption of viable cells. The conditions in the food (or raw materials) or its storage temperature will influence the ability of toxigenic pathogens to produce toxin. After its formation, handling and processing (e.g. heating) may influence the levels of pre-formed toxin remaining in food. Staphylococcal toxin is very heat stable, whereas botulinum toxin is not heat stable. The toxin-producing cells may be killed by processing but the conditions needed to achieve this may not lead to inactivation of any toxin formed, therefore the possibility of pre-formed toxin may go unrecognised if only microbiological data from end-product testing is obtained.

Sub-step 4.7 - Attributes of the food

The compositition of the food (e.g. fatty) and the consumption pattern (e.g. eating with an empty stomach) may directly affect the ability of the agent to cause harm. These factors are important if they allow the harmful agent to avoid the host defence mechanisms (such as stomach acidity or surface barriers) and reach a part of the gut where it can become established or be absorbed. Under these circumstances illness will be caused at lower doses and the severity or speed of onset of illness, caused by a given dose, will increase. In some cases, processing before consumption, e.g. heating or freezing, may also influence the virulence of an infectious pathogen (see Sub-step 4.6). If the microorganisms are protected, e.g. enclosed in fat, then their infectivity or resistance to heating may increase.

Sub-step 4.8 - Sensitivity of host

Illness from a given dose may occur more frequently or be more severe for elderly or immuno-compromised individuals, pregnant women or members of the population with different nutritional or socio-economic status. The description or construction of a consuming population needs to reflect the sensitivities of its members and quantifying the subsets within the population can lead to a more robust assessment. Where such information cannot be obtained, it is important to record the assumptions made about the population.

Sub-step 4.9 - Handling of variability and uncertainty

Variability

Many of the most important factors influencing the level of risk will vary. Taking account of variability (e.g. differences in virulence of micro-organisms or sensitivity of consumers) will improve the quality of a risk estimate. Additional data will better define the distribution or range of sensitivities, consumption patterns, risks or hazards. Variability will reduce the value of any 'point' risk estimate and additional data will have a very limited effect on improving the usefulness of such a risk assessment. Risk estimates are improved if the amount of data used and its variability are specified to indicate the extremes of the range and a typical value or a statistical distribution. This will lead to a range of risk estimates describing the range of risks present for particular circumstances or combinations of micro-organisms, foods and consumers.

Uncertainty

In practice, risk assessments will usually be done with incomplete data, but they should always use the best data available. For any product, specific valid data may not be found concerning:- the incidence of the pathogen, the hazardous dose, the distribution of sensitivity and likely severity of symptoms in consumers of the product and any effects of customer handling prior to consumption. As any realistic risk assessment needs to take account of all these factors, the assumptions made need to be specified in a way that allows the user to understand their basis and their effect on the conclusions i.e. over or underestimating the risks. The effects of uncertainty will be reduced by the use of better or more relevant data. In some cases this can be acquired relatively easily (e.g. data on the effects of heating according to instructions on pathogen numbers or from records of the incidence of microorganisms in the product). Other types of data such as the incidence of sensitivity in a population or the potential for cross-contamination in the home may also be used.

C. Illustration of information required and used for MRA

The following landscape tables provide an illustration of the information required and used for qualitative and quantitative risk assessments, with reference to two published examples. It is important to appreciate that the published examples used were not necessarily conducted as practical risk assessments, but published as part of studies into the development of MRA procedures. This means that some of the cells in the table are blank as some issues will not have been included in these published MRAs. Also, the comments presented, therefore, are not intended as criticism but to help highlight the benefits and limitations of particular approaches.

Table 4 - Illustration of information required and used for qualitative and quantitative risk assessments (MRA), with published examples

STEP 4 - Hazard Characterisation	Type of Risk Assessment: Qualitative Risk Assessment and Comparative Risk Assessment	Type of Risk Assessment: Quantitative Risk Assessment	Examples of published MRAs:
			Example 1. *Salmonelia* in poultry. Brown *et al.*, 1998. **Example 2**. *E coli* O157 in beef hamburgers. Cassin *et al.*, 1998
4.1 Adverse health effects	Descriptions of sensitivity, severity, end-points etc for the range of consumers of the product should be used. Wherever possible information from specialist agencies, journals and health ministry reporting should be used and consumers (age etc.) should be described	Quantitative descriptions of sensitivity (dose-response), sensitivity, severity, end-points etc for the range of consumers of the product should be used. This should include directly relevant information from specialist agencies, journals and health ministries.	**Example 1** Not mentioned specifically **Example 2** This is considered as HUS or mortality, and is described in *3.1 Hazard Identification*
4.2 Dose response			**Example 1** Several authors have found it convenient to describe infection with the Beta-Poisson distribution, which has a cumulative percentage given by: $I(x) = 100 - \frac{100}{\left(1 + \frac{x}{\beta}\right)^{\alpha}}$ **Example 2** Covered in section *3.3 Dose-response assessment*. "The dose-response model estimated the probability of illness resulting from a certain level of exposure. The model used was based on the Beta-Poisson model for infection."

	Qualitative Risk Assessment and Comparative Risk Assessment	Quantitative Risk Assessment	Examples of published MRAs:
4.3 End-points and sensitivity of the host	4.1, 4.2, 4.3, 4.4 (continued)	4.1, 4.2, 4.3, 4.4 (continued)	**Example 1** "For a comprehensive risk characterisation, infection should be ranked by severity levels, especially where consumers include susceptible groups. This can only be undertaken when sufficient published information is available. Currently in this QRA, infection encompasses all degrees of human response." **Exmaple 2** HUS and mortality considered in children and healthy adults
4.4 Quantification			**Example 1** YES, see dose response **Example 2** "The model predicted a probability of HUS of 3.7e-6 and probability of mortality of 1.7e-7 per meal for the very young.
4.6 Status of micro-organism and	The impact of processing, product composition (e.g. fat protection) and eating habits on infectivity, toxigenisis and toxin persistence should be included and noted in the risk estimate. For a comparative risk assessment this information must also be available for the benchmark product. E.g. fat enrobement may reduce heat sensitivity and increase invasiveness. Where the inclusion of specific, published data on infectivity or microbial resistance leads to changes in the risk assessment, the source of the data and the conclusions drawn should be quoted	Specific, published data on altered infectivity or toxigenesis may change the hazardous dose from d_1 to d_2. Specific data relevant to hazards, products and consumers must be incorporated and the source of this data and the conclusions drawn should be quoted	**Example 2** Fatty trimmings were considered to be an important source of the organism, although mention of fat content not specifically mentioned
4.7 Attributes of the food			

	Qualitative Risk Assessment and Comparative Risk Assessment	**Quantitative Risk Assessment**	**Examples of published MRAs:**
4.8 Sensitivity of the host			**Example 1**."Individuals who would become ill by ingesting a low dose are termed susceptible, and usually include children, the elderly, pregnant women, and immuno-compromised adults. Healthy adults may not be harmed by much larger doses." "Dose-response models have been published for different serotypes, based either on data from healthy adults, or a large spectrum of people from the population. In addition, the dose response of children has been estimated from limited internal data. The graphical interface allows any of these potential consumer groups to be selected and a risk assessment recalculated automatically." **Example 2** This was considered in terms of children and healthy adults
4.9 Uncertainty	There will be stated uncertainty in this type of risk estimate. It will only be valid for the defined consumer groups. Uncertainty will be reduced by use of better process/product and consumer data during the preceding stages. *For a comparative risk assessment, data must be available for the benchmark product.*	Uncertainty should be minimised by use of good process and product data allowing the use of kinetic models during the exposure assessment and producing likely concentrations of micro-organisms or toxin and profiling of the consumers of the product linked to dose responses.	**Example 1** Mentioned but not dealt with in the model "In some cases it may not be possible to describe accurately the dose-response due to insufficient data or high variability in population response. Because of the uncertainty introduced by these two sources of variability the focus is on relative changes in population response due to product and process modifications, rather than the actual computed values"

Step 5 - Risk Characterisation

Risk characterisation is an estimation of the likelihood of adverse health effects occurring in a given community, and their severity, based on hazard identification and exposure assessment. The estimate should ideally be quantitative, but can be qualitative. The degree of uncertainty must be recorded.

Bringing together the information of the previous stages, it provides an estimate, qualitative or quantitative, of risk to a given population or sub-population.

The degree of confidence of the final estimation of risk will depend on the factors considered and their uncertainty identified in all the previous stages.

A. Description

Risk characterisation is not just a mathematical issue, expert judgement on the contribution of data to the level of risk is required. The analysis is carried out to review where extra input in terms of expertise or knowledge/information is required. Data needs to be structured to give high, low or no confidence.

The quality of the information used needs to be addressed - does it matter if the wrong dose-response curve is used? There is a need to be able to test the robustness of the Risk Assessment by, for example, changing the parameters and noting what effect this has.

This implies that a (mathematical) modelling approach may be suitable. If possible quantitative data should be used for this, if not, then qualitative data should be used, in which case this must be stated.

B. Commentary text

Risk characterisation is an estimation of the likelihood and severity of adverse health effects occurring in a given group of people, based on hazard identification, hazard characterisation and exposure assessment. The estimate should ideally be quantitative, but can be qualitative. The uncertainty must be indicated. The dependence of the risk estimate on key factors must be indicated. The validity of the risk estimate must be assessed against experience.

Prerequisites

This step (Risk Characterisation) brings together information from all the previous steps, and requires a broad range of skills. Even for a qualitative risk assessment it involves the manipulation of uncertainty and variability, so that someone deeply familiar with these statistical concepts is essential.

This is not however, just a mathematical issue, expert judgement is required. Expertise in microbiology and in the process under consideration will also be required. This is clear for a quantitative assessment where the likelihood of different parameter values must be assessed. It is equally essential for qualitative assessments where mathematics may be unable to help in combining information and only experience and skill can help.

Procedure

The Risk Characterisation can be divided into a number of stages

(a) Combining Exposure Assessment and Hazard Characterisation
As indicated in Figure 4, Exposure Assessment and Hazard Characterisation each result in a likelihood and these must be combined in Risk Characterisation.
(b) Summarising the risk
(c) Sensitivity analysis
(d) Variability in risk
(e) Uncertainty
(f) Validation against experience

Figure 4 - A Breakdown of Inputs into Risk Characterisation

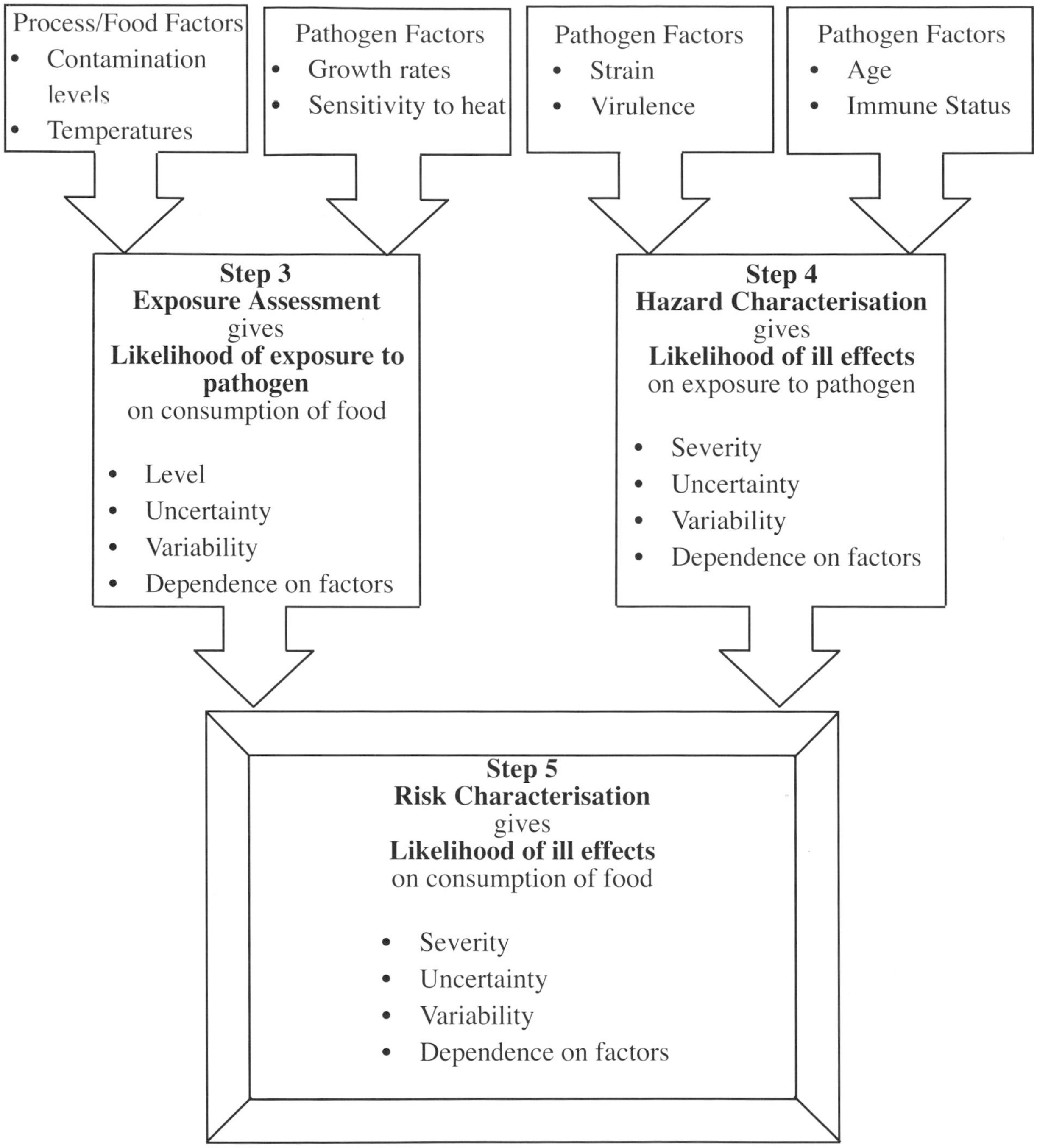

It is unlikely that the results of Steps 3 and 4 are simple numbers. Likelihood of exposure and likelihood of ill effects are each likely to depend on the level of exposure. In a fully quantitative risk assessment these might be expressed graphically, for example:

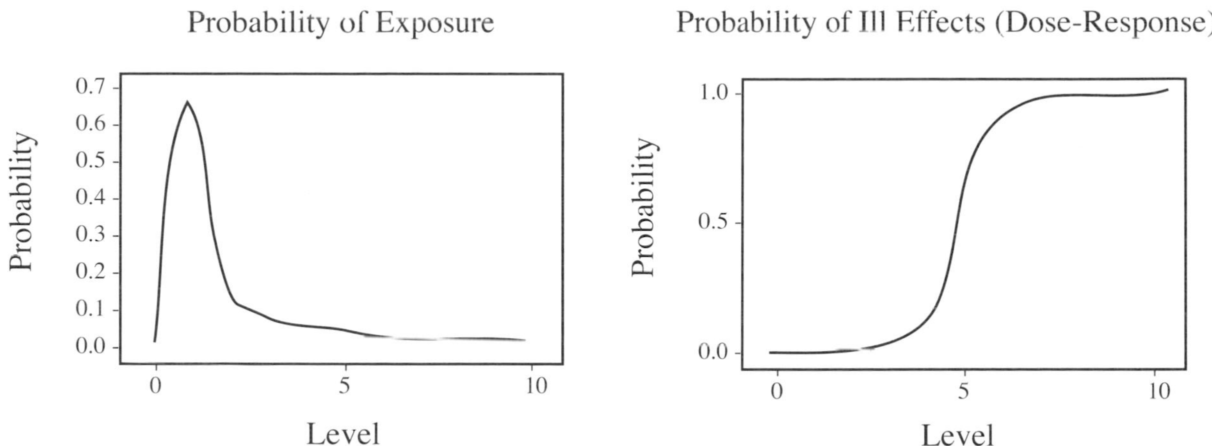

Even these will not capture the complete output of the respective steps. There will be uncertainty associated with the curves. There may also be variability. For example, the dose-response curve may reflect the susceptibility of the "average" person, but there may be substantial groups of people with different susceptibility.

In the ideal, but unlikely, case of a fully quantitative risk assessment in which all factors are quantitatively described, probably as statistical probability distributions, and all mechanisms are fully understood and represented as mathematical models, the outputs of Exposure Assessment and Hazard Characterisation may be mathematical expressions. In that case they can, at least in principle, be combined into a single mathematical expression.

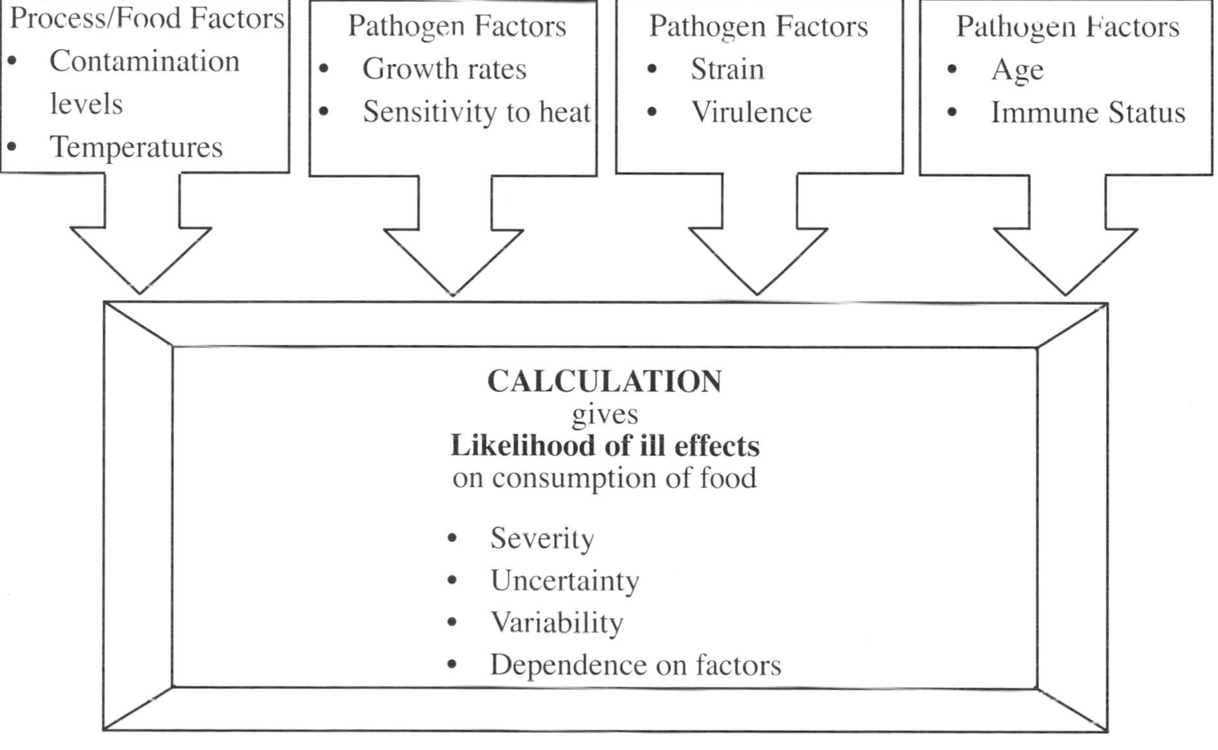

Such mathematical risk assessments would require a great deal of time and skill to construct and will generally be developed as strategic tools. Their benefits lie in their completeness and flexibility. With due regard to the constraints and assumptions implicit in such a model, once it has been constructed it could be used to answer a range of "what if" questions and can be of great benefit in product and process development, and in problem solving.

This kind of "pure mathematical" risk assessment is extremely rare. At the other extreme the outputs of steps 3 and 4 may be entirely non-numerical, in which case their combination is likely to be totally non-mathematical. Generally the situation will be between the two extremes with some text, and some numerical or mathematical information.

Whatever the kind of information being used it is essential to involve a range of skills. Even in a fully mathematical risk assessment it is essential to have a complete grasp of the food technology and microbiological concepts being modelled. Mathematical modelling is an art, with many choices for the modeller. If relevant experts do not closely advise the leader of the risk assessment, inappropriate judgements may be made.

Even in a totally text based risk assessment it is essential to have a deep understanding of the statistical concepts of probability, uncertainty, and confidence. Risk characterisation involves combining probabilities of unlikely events. If this is done injudiciously it can lead to such unlikely combinations of worst cases that the risk assessment becomes unrealistic. Alternatively the risk assessment can lose its objectivity. While combination of qualitative data may not involve mathematical manipulations it often requires a higher level of mathematical understanding than quantitative data.

a) Summarising the risk

Whatever the type of data, the combination of likelihoods will give quite a complex "model", whether a purely mathematical model, or a conceptual model represented in text, or some combination of the two. In any case it will be too complex to directly provide the output required by the Statement of Purpose (step 1) indicated above; the likelihood of ill effects will probably depend on factors to do with the food and the process, the pathogen, and the person, and be expressed in a relatively complex manner, probably graphically. It is likely that the decision-maker will need some summary on which to base the decision.

There is a range of options available to summarise the risk. Their respective benefits should have been considered at Step 1 - Statement of Purpose when specifying the nature of the output required. However, a final decision cannot be made until the quality of the final data is known. It is also important to ensure that no features of the data important to the decision-maker will be lost.

Some ways of summarising the overall risk are:

- **arithmetic mean** - this is unlikely to be meaningful
- **median** - risk experienced by 50% of the population
- **mode** - most common value of risk
- **"maximum"** - risk experienced by "very few" (5%?, 1%?, 0.1%, 1 in a million?)

An inappropriate summary can be very misleading. It is important to have a clear understanding of the concepts involved, even for a "text" assessment.

b) Sensitivity analysis

It may be that the estimated final risk is not substantially affected by credible variations in the various factors, parameters, assumptions, models etc. It is more likely that some have a large effect and some a lesser effect.

Identification of process and food factors that have a substantial effect on the final risk is an important benefit of risk assessment. It allows effective direction of risk reduction measures, and targeted consideration of the effect of variability.

Assessment of the effect of parameter values, assumptions and models on the final risk assessment is often the only way of transferring uncertainties in them through to the final value. Often this can effectively be performed by varying these and observing the effect on the final risk assessment.

c) Variability in risk

Any summary "loses" information. Although the summary may convey an "average" or "overall" risk, the risk may be very different for some groups of people, or for some circumstances. Variability in factors relating to process, food, pathogen or people can feed through to variability in final risk. The sensitivity analysis is an important guide in planning assessment of variability.

If variability in a factor has been included in its uncertainty, it will feed through to uncertainty in the final risk.

If variability in a factor has been identified and fed through the process the final risk will be dependent on source factors. For example this might result in different final risks for different groups of people, or an expression for final risk which depends on storage life.

In such a case it is important to clearly report the dependence, and the variation in risk between different circumstances or groups.

d) Uncertainty

The uncertainty expresses the range of values that may credibly be true. It may be that the "best" estimate would lead to one decision, but that uncertainties are so large that a value leading to another decision is quite credible. It is essential to accompany any indication of risk with an indication of the associated uncertainty.

In principle it is possible to estimate the final uncertainty by tracking the uncertainties of all the "inputs" to the risk assessments, modifying and combining the uncertainties as the inputs are modified and combined. Often this is impractical and the effects of input uncertainties on the output must be estimated by sensitivity analysis.

Combination of uncertainties requires care and skill as individually unlikely circumstances are combined. Particular attention must be paid to two aspects: -

i) Circumstances, which are individually unlikely but credible, may, in combination, be so unlikely as to be unrealistic. It is important not to simply combine "worst cases" without consideration of the final probability.

ii) Correlation between factors may make some combinations very much more or very much less likely.

e) Validation against experience

It is essential to ensure that the results of the risk assessment accord with common sense and with experience.

The following landscape tables provide an illustration of the information required and used for qualitative and quantitative risk assessments, with reference to two published examples. It is important to appreciate that the published examples used were not necessarily conducted as practical risk assessments, but published as part of studies into the development of MRA procedures. This means that some of the cells in the table are blank as some issues will not have been included in these published MRAs. Also, the comments presented, therefore, are not intended as criticism but to help highlight the benefits and limitations of particular approaches.

Table 5 - Illustration of information required and used for qualitative and quantitative risk assessments (MRA), with published examples

STEP 5 - Risk Characterisation	Type of Risk Assessment		
	Qualitative Risk Assessment and Comparative Risk Assessment	**Quantitative Risk Assessment**	**Examples of published MRAs:**
	A qualitative estimate will be produced with some uncertainty; it will indicate the impact of a range of circumstances on the safety of the product and the circumstances under which the Risk Characterisation is valid. E.g. product used by typical and sensitive consumers in accordance with the instructions will be safe, but storage above 10°C may give a product potentially hazardous for sensitive consumers. For a comparative risk assessment this should be indicated for the benchmark product and the origins or causes of increase or reduction in risk for the new product should be presented. A quantitative estimate will be produced with a description of variability and uncertainty, it will indicate the probability of the product causing harm under the range of circumstances described. E.g. 1% of product containing >10^4 *Salmonella*/g which may receive a heat treatment below 70°C x 1 minutes will be hazardous to 5% of consumers. Therefore 5 packs/10 million may be hazardous.		**Example 1**. *Salmonella* in poultry. Brown *et al*., 1998. **Example 2**. *E coli* O157 in beef hamburgers. Cassin *et al*., 1998
	A qualitative or comparative estimate of risk will be produced with associated uncertainty. The estimate will indicate the range of circumstances under which the product is safe, or whether it is more or less safe than the benchmark product, the range of concentrations of the hazard covered and their impact on consumer sensitivity. E.g. among consumers of the product in the UK, DH data can indicate the frequency of illness associated with particular products and consumer types.	A quantitative estimate will be produced with specified uncertainty. The sensitivity of consumers should be described mathematically and it will indicate the range of circumstances under which the product is safe and how safety is influenced by the range of consumer sensitivity evident from food-poisoning statistics and case information. E.g. a study of food-poisoning among old people linked to partially processed products in the UK showed that 10% are infected by <10cells, 50% by <1000 cells and 90% by 10,000 cells.	

	Qualitative Risk Assessment and Comparative Risk Assessment	Quantitative Risk Assessment	Examples of published MRAs:
	Qualitative risk estimate can lead to conservative supply chain and usage conditions to protect consumer safety. If there is high uncertainty or variable information, conditions may be unnecessarily severe. E.g. the conclusions of this assessment will protect typical consumers and those who will not be infected by 1000 cells/portion. Where a comparative risk assessment has been done, uncertainty will originate both from the benchmark product and from the changes made in the new product. Any areas of particular uncertainty should be highlighted and the basis of the consideration of the benchmark product as safe should be explained	Quantitative risk estimate can provide milder products, optimised supply chain and usage conditions protecting consumer safety, if there is low uncertainty with reliable kinetics and information which are fully analysed. The conclusions of this type of assessment will cover the most sensitive consumers provided that processing conditions are maintained within specified limits, e.g. the infectious pathogen specification in raw material quality may be relaxed 10-fold without an increase in risk. It is difficult to validate the output of QRA models.	
	Specialist journal, expert opinion, prescriptive rules or guidelines data is used to interpret and identify principles relevant to product and circumstances. *For the benchmark product used in a comparative risk assessment, the quality of information used must be examined in the same way.*	Specialist journal, predictive kinetics, and prescriptive rules or guidelines, expressly relevant and interpreted for product, consumer and circumstances	
	Comparison of range of qualitative estimates with experience, records and reported incidence of complaints and food-poisoning. E.g. this product is typical of other products in the market place and their compliant/food-poisoning record is 'n'/million portions.	Generate range of quantitative estimates and compare with reported incidence/complaints for specific and similar products and consumers. It is unlikely that more detailed data will be available, therefore this product is typical of other products in the market place and their compliant/ food-poisoning record is 'n'/million portions.	

Step 6 - Produce a Formal Report

The risk assessment should be fully and systematically documented. To ensure transparency, the final report should indicate in particular any constraints and assumptions relative to the risk assessment. To ensure transparency, the report should be made available to stakeholders or independent parties on request from the company.

A Description

Once the Risk Assessment has been carried out, there is a need to record that everything has been done in a systematic way. To ensure transparency, the final report should indicate any constraints and assumptions relative to the risk assessment. This will allow the assessment to be audited and reviewed. The report enables the risk assessment and its findings to be communicated to all interested parties.

B. Commentary text

Sub-step 6.1 - Full, systematic report

Essentially a report which comments and considers the steps and sub-steps illustrated above for the MRA in question.

Sub-step 6.2 - Indicate constraints and assumptions

All the constraints and assumptions used in carrying out the MRA need to be formally recorded.

C. Illustration of information required and used for MRA

The following landscape tables provide an illustration of the information required and used for qualitative and quantitative risk assessments, with reference to two published examples. It is important to appreciate that the published examples used were not necessarily conducted as practical risk assessments, but published as part of studies into the development of MRA procedures. This means that some of the cells in the table are blank as some issues will not have been included in these published MRAs. Also, the comments presented, therefore, are not intended as criticism but to help highlight the benefits and limitations of particular approaches.

Table 6 - Illustration of information required and used for qualitative and quantitative risk assessments (MRA), with published examples

STEP 6 - Formal Report	**Type of Risk Assessment**		**Examples of published MRAs:**
	Qualitative Risk Assessment and comparative Risk Assessment	**Quantitative Risk Assessment**	**Example 1**. *Salmonella* in poultry. Brown *et al.*, 1998. **Example 2**. *E coli* O157 in beef hamburgers. Cassin *et al.*, 1998
6.1 Report type	The conclusion and risk estimate should be described in understandable *(comparative)* terms. Uncertainty, assumptions and variability should also be described along with the conditions and types of consumers considered.	The risk estimate should be described as a probability Uncertainty; assumptions and variability should be quantified. The populations of consumers considered should be described in statistical terms for sensitivity etc.	**6.1 Full systematic report?** **Example 1** NO **Example 2** NO (This would not be expected in a publication)
6.2 Indicate constraints and assumptions			**Example 1.** Mentioned in each relevant section. For example: • "During home cooking it is assumed that heat is only supplied to one face at a time, and a single face is exposed to the heat source for 70% of the cook time and the opposite face for 30%, to simulate grilling or pan-frying." • For the risk calculation it is assumed that each consumer eats a whole portion of chicken and one only. • In this example the product has been kept frozen, and therefore the numbers entering the heat process are assumed to be the same as in the raw material • It is assumed that the kinetics of inactivation in these frozen products are not significantly different from the published values • It is also assumed that any survivors are infectious. **Example 2.** This is mentioned throughout the text. For example: Faeces are the major source of *E coli* O157:H7; all (100%) microbes will potentially give rise to illness; "the prevalence of *E coli* O157:H7 on carcasses was assumed to be proportional to the prevalence of animals shedding the pathogen....

SECTION 5 - REFERENCES

5.1 Case Studies (Published MRAs)

Subject	Relevant references
Listeria	Buchanan *et al.*, 1997; Farber *et al.*, 1996; Notermans *et al.*, 1998
Escherichia coli O157: H7	Cassin *et al.*, 1998
Bacillus cereus	Notermans *et al.*, 1997; Zwietering *et al.*, 1996
Salmonella	Brown *et al.*, 1998; USDA, 1997; USDA (FSIS), 1998; Todd, 1996; Berends *et al.*,1996
Campylobacter	Medema *et al.*, 1996
Eggs and egg products	USDA, 1997; USDA (FSIS), 1998; Todd, 1996
Poultry industry	Brown *et al.*, 1998; Oscar, 1998
Sous-vide products	Barker *et al.*, 1999

5.2 Useful Websites

The following web-sites are useful sources of information on: MRA in general; data for those wishing to carry out an MRA; regulatory information; and MRAs that are currently being undertaken.

CAST (Council for Agricultural Science & Technology)	http://www.cast-science.org/
CCFRA:	http://www.campden.co.uk
CFSAN:	http://vm.cfsan.fda.gov
EUROPEAN UNION:	http://www.europa.eu.int/
FSIS:	http://www.fsis.usda.gov/
ILSI:	http://www.ilsi.org/europe.html
Ontario Ministry of Agriculture, Food & Rural Affairs, Canada	http://www.gov.on.ca
PHLS:	http://www.phls.co.uk/
SRA (Society of Risk Analysis)	http://www.sra.org
WHO:	http://www.who.int/fsf/index.htm

5.3 References

Advisory Committee on Dangerous Pathogens (1996). Microbiological Risk Assessment: An interim report. June. HMSO ISBN 0 11 321990 3.

Anon (1989). Official Control of Foodstuffs Directive 89/397/EEC. Official Journal of the European Communities, L186, 14. 06. 1989, 23.

Anon (1993). The Assistance to the Commission and Co-operation by the Member states in the Scientific Examination of Questions relating to Food Directive 93/5/EEC, Official Journal of the European Communities, L52, 25.02. 1993, 18.

Barker, G.C., Talbot, N.L.C. and Peck, M.W. (1999). Microbiological Risk Assessment for sous-vide foods. Third European Symposium on sous-vide proceedings, March 25-26, 1999.

Berends, B. R., Urlings, H. A. P., Snijders, J. M. A. and Van Knapen, F. (1996). Identification and quantification of risk factors in animal management and transport regarding *Salmonella* spp in pigs. Int. J. Food Microbiol., **30**, 37-53

Berends, B. R., Van Knapen, F. and Snijders, J.M. A. (1996). Suggestions for the construction, analysis and use of descriptive epidemiological models for the modernisation of meat inspection. Int. J. Food Microbiol., **30**, 27-36

Bernard, D. and Stringer, M.F. (1997). 'Microbiological Risk Assessment - CCFRA/NFPA Situation Report'.

Borch, E., Nesbakken, T. and Christensen, H. (1996). Hazard identification in swine slaughter with respect to foodborne bacteria. Int. J. Food Microbiol., **30**, 9-25.

Boroush, M. (ACS/RFF): (1998). Understanding Risks Analysis. A short guide for health, safety and environment policy making.

Brown, M. H., Davies, K. W., Billon, C.M.P., Adair, C. and McClure, P. J. (1998). Quantitative Microbiological Risk Assessment: Principles applied to determining the comparative risk of salmonellosis from chicken products. J. Food Prot., **61** (11), 1446-1453.

Bryan, F.L. and Doyle, M.P. (1995). Health risks and consequences of *Salmonella* and *Campylobacter jejuni* in raw poultry. J. Food Prot., **58**, 326-344.

Buchanan, R.L. (1995). The role of microbiological criteria and risk assessment in HACCP. Food Microbiol., **12**, 421-424.

Buchanan, R.L. (1997). National Advisory Committee on Microbiological Criteria for Foods Principles of Risk Assessment for illnesses caused by foodborne biological agents. J. Food Prot., **60**, 1417-1419.

Buchanan, R.L., Damert, W.G., Whiting, R.C. and Van Schothorst, M. (1997). Use of epidemiologic and food survey data to estimate a purposefully conservative dose-response relationship for *Listeria monocytogenes* levels and incidence of listeriosis. J. Food Prot., **60** (8), 918-922

Buchanan, R.L. and Whiting, R.C. (1998). Risk Assessment: A means for linking HACCP plans and public health. J. Food Prot., **61** (11), pp. 1531-1534.

Cassin, M.H., Lammerding, A.M., Todd, E.C.D., Ross, W. and McColl, R.S. (1998). Quantitative risk assessment for *Escherichia coli* O157: H7 in ground beef hamburgers.
Int. J. Food Microbiol., **41**, 21-44.

CCFRA (1997). HACCP: A Practical Guide (Second Edition) Technical Manual no. 38.
Ed. S. Leaper.

Codex Alimentarius Commission (1996). Draft Principles and Guidelines for the Application of Microbiological Risk Assessment. August

Codex Alimentarius Commission (1998). Draft Principles and Guidelines for the Conduct of Microbiological Risk Assessment. ALINOR 99/13A.

Codex Alimentarius Commission (1999) Report on the 32nd session of the Codex committee on food hygiene. Washington D C 29 November - 4 December 1999. Alinorm 01/13 Appendix IV. Proposed draft principles and guidelines for the conduct of Microbiological Risk Management at step3.

Coleman, M.E. and Marks, H.M. (1999). Qualitative and quantitative risk assessment. Food Control, **10**, 289-297.

Crockett, C.S., Haas, C.N., Fazil, A., Rose, J.B. and Gerba, C.P. (1996). Prevalence of shigellosis in the US: consistency with dose-response information. Inter. J. Food Microbiol., **30**, 87-99.

Department of Health (1997) 'Communicating about Risks to Public Health - Pointers to Good Practice', November.

European Commission (1997). 'Principles for the development of risk assessment of microbiological hazards under directive 93/43/EEC concerning the hygiene of foodstuffs'. September. (Available through the Europa server (http://europa.eu.int).

FAO/WHO (1995). Expert consultation on the application of risk analysis to food standard issues - recommendations to CODEX. March.

FAO/WHO. (1997). Risk Management and Food Safety. Rome, January.

Farber, J.M., Ross, W.H. and Harwig, J. (1996). Health risk assessment of *Listeria monocytogenes* in Canada. Inter. J. Food Microbiol., **30**, 145-156.

Gale, P., Young, C., Stanfield, G. and Oakes, D. (1998). A review: Development of a risk assessment for BSE in the aquatic environment. J. Appl. Microbiol., **84**, 467-477.

Gerba, C.P., Rose, J.B. and Haas, C.N. (1996). Sensitive populations: who is at the greatest risk? Int. J. Food Microbiol., **30**, 87-99.

Griffith, C., Worsfold, D. and Mitchell, R. (1998). Food preparation, risk communication and the consumer. Food Control, **9** (4), 225-232.

Haas, C.N., Rose, J.B. and Gerba, C.P. (1999). Quantitative Microbiological Risk Assessment. John Wiley & Sons, New York

Hathaway, S.C. (1997). Development of Food Safety Risk Assessment Guidelines for foods of animal origin in international trade. J. Food Prot., **60** (11), 1432-1438.

Hitchins, A.D. (1996). Assessment of alimentary exposure to *Listeria monocytogenes*. Int. J. Food Microbiol., **30**, 71-85.

International Commission on Microbiological Specifications for Foods (ICMSF): (1998). Potential application of risk assessment techniques to microbiological issues related to international trade in food and food products. J. Food Prot., **61** (8), 1075-1086.

International Life Sciences Institute (ILSI) European Branch (1998a). Food Safety Management Tools. Eds. J.L. Jouve, M.F. Stringer, and A.C. Baird-Parker.

ILSI (1998b). "Principles for the development of risk assessment of microbiological hazards under directive 93/43/EEC concerning the hygiene of foodstuffs". European Commission. September 1997. Available through the European server (http://europa.eu.int).

Lammerding, A. M. (1996). Microbial Food Safety Risk Assessment: Principles and Practice. Proceedings, Xth International Conference on Food Safety, ASEPT, Laval.

Lammerding, A.M. and Paoli, G.M. (1997). Quantitative risk assessment: An emerging tool for emerging foodborne pathogens. Emerging Infectious Diseases, 3, 4, October-December

Marks, H. and Coleman, M. (1998). Estimating distributions of numbers of organisms in food products. J. Food Prot., **61** (11), 1535-1540.

McNab, W.B. (1998). Review - A general framework illustrating an approach to quantitative microbial food safety risk assessment. J. Food Prot., **61** (9), 1216-1228.

Mead, G.C. (1982). Microbiology of poultry and game birds, pp 67-101. *In*: M.H. Brown (Ed). Meat Microbiology. Applied Science Publ. Ltd, London

Medema, G.J., Teunis, P.F.M., Havelaar, A.H. and Haas, C.N. (1996). Assessment of the dose-response relationship of *Campylobacter jejuni*. Int. J. Food Microbiol., **30**, 101-111.

Mitchell, R.T. Practical Microbiological Risk Analysis. How to Assess, Manage and Communicate Microbiological Risks in Foods (in press)

National Advisory Committee on Microbiological Criteria for Foods (NCAMCF): (1998). Principles of risk assessment for illness caused by foodborne biological agents. J. Food Prot., **61** (8), 1071-1074.

Needleman, J. (1988). Sources and policy implications of uncertainty in risk assessment. Statistical Science, **3**, 3, 328-338

Nickelsen, L. and Jakobsen, M. (1997). Quantitative Risk Analysis of aflatoxin toxicity for the consumers of 'kenkey' - a fermented maize product. Food Control, **8**, 149 - 159.

Notermans, S., Zwietering, M.H. and Mead, G.C. (1994). The HACCP concept: identification of potentially hazardous microorganisms. Food Microbiol., **11**, 203-214.

Notermans, S., Gallhoff, G., Zwietering, M.H. and Mead, G.C. (1995). The HACCP concept: specification of criteria using quantitative risk assessment. Food Microbiol **12**, 81-90.

Notermans, S. and Mead, G.C. (1996). Incorporation of elements of quantitative risk analysis in the HACCP system. Int. J. Food Microbiol., **30**, 157-173

Notermans, S., Mead, G.C. and Jouve, J.L. (1996). Food products and consumer protection: A conceptual approach and a glossary of terms. Int. J. Food Microbiol., **30**, 175 -183.

Notermans, S. and Teunis, P. (1996). Quantitative risk analysis and the production of microbiologically safe food: an introduction. Int. J. Food Microbiol., **30**, 9-25.

Notermans, S., Dufrenne, J., Teunis, P., Beumer, R., te Giffel, M., and Peeters Weem, P. (1997). A risk assessment study of *Bacillus cereus* present in pasteurised milk. Food Microbiol., **14**, 143-151.

Notermans, S., Dufrenne, J., Teunis, P. and Chackraborty, T. (1998). Studies on the risk assessment of *Listeria monocytogenes*. J. Food Prot., **61** (2), 244-248.

Notermans, S., Nauta, M.J., Jansen, J., Jouve, J.L. and Mead, G.C. (1998). A risk assessment approach to evaluating food safety based on product surveillance. Food Control, **9** (4), 217-223.

Panisello, P.J. and Quantick, P.C. (1998). Opinion: HACCP and its implementation. The need for an international microbiological hazard database. Food Sci. Technol. Today, **12** (3), 130-133.

Oscar, T.P. (1998). The development of a risk assessment model for use in the poultry industry. J. Food Safety, **18**, 371-381.

Phillips, B., Rutherford, N., Gorsuch, T., Mabey, M., Looker, N. and Boggiano, R. (1995). How indicators can perform for hazard and risk management in risk assessments of food premises. Food Sci. Technol. Today, **9** (1), 19-30.

Scientific Committee for Food (1997). Outcome of discussions. Opinion on principles for the development of risk assessment of microbiological hazards under the hygiene of foodstuffs directive 03/43/EEC (expressed on 13th June 1997).

The Scientific Committee on Medical Products and Medical Devices (1998). Opinion on the risk quantification for CJD transmission via substances of human origin. October.

Serra, J.A., Domenech, E., Escriche, I. and Martorelli, S. (1999). Risk assessment and critical control points from the production perspective. Int. J. Food Microbiol., **46**, 9-26.

Todd, E.C.D. (1978). Foodborne disease in six countries - a comparison. J. Food Prot., **41**: 559-565

Todd, E.C.D. (1996). Risk assessment of use of cracked eggs in Canada. Int. J. Food Microbiol., **30**, 125-143.

US Department of Agriculture (1997). Parameter values for a risk assessment of *Salmonella* Enteritidis in shell eggs and egg products. August.

US Department of Agriculture Food Safety and Inspection Service (1998). *Salmonella* Enteritidis Risk Assessment: Shell Eggs and Egg Products, report 268.

Van Gerwen, S.J.C. (2000). Microbiological Risk Assessment of Food. A stepwise quantitative risk assessment as a tool in the production of microbiologically safe food. PhD Thesis. Wageningen University.

Van Gerwen, S.J.C. and Zwietering, M.H. (1998). Growth and inactivation models to be used in quantitative Risk Assessments. J. Food Prot., **61** (11), 1541-1549.

Van Schothorst, M. (1997). Practical approaches to risk assessment. J. Food Prot., **60** (11), 1439-1443.

Van Schothorst, M. (1998). Principles for the establishment of microbiological food safety objectives and related control measures. Food Control, **9** (6), 379-384.

Vose, D.J. (1998). The applications of quantitative risk assessment to microbial food safety. J. Food Prot., **61** (5), 640-648.

Voysey, P.A (1999). Aspects of Microbiological Risk Assessment. New Food., **2**, 3-13

Zwietering, M.H., de Wit, J.C. and Notermans, S. (1996). Application of predictive microbiology to estimate the number of *Bacillus cereus* in pasteurised milk at the point of consumption. Int. J. Food Microbiol., **30**, 55-70.

APPENDICES

Appendix 1

Interaction between the government's and a company's food safety activities.

This diagram shows the relationship between government and company food safety activities. When originally conceived, Risk analysis was placed under governmental activities, so that Food Safety Objectives could be set. It is now apparent that companies wish to have a part to play in the process of Risk Analysis.

Appendix 2

A technique for a simple Risk Profile

This appendix outlines the technique for carrying out a Risk Profile.

APPENDIX 1: Interaction between the government's and a company's food safety activities (ILSI, 1998a)

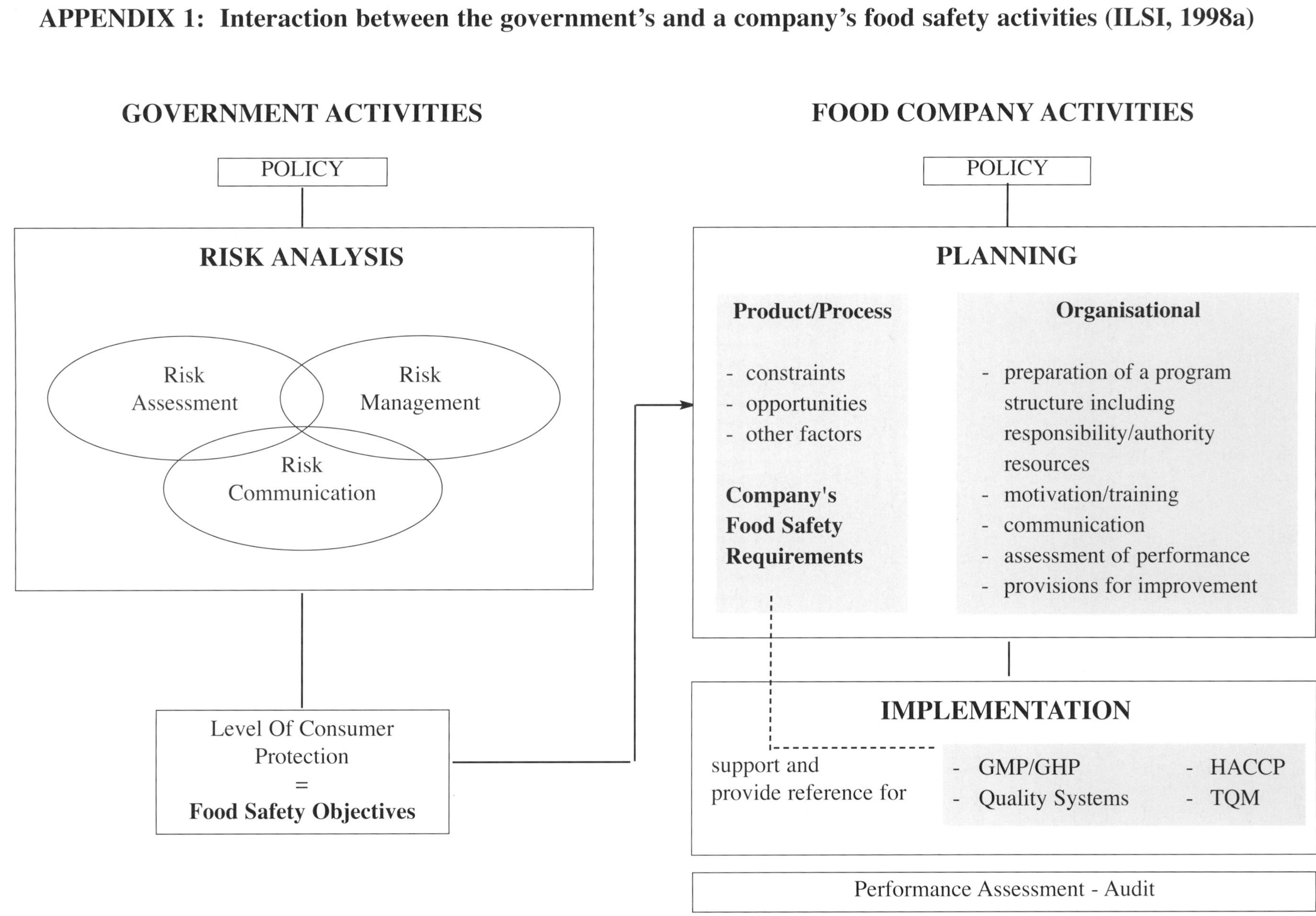

APPENDIX 2 - A TECHNIQUE FOR A SIMPLE RISK PROFILE

A2.1 Introduction to the "Simple Risk Profile"

A simple paper-based approach to risk assessment is given in this Appendix. The text and questionnaire "**Quick" Risk Assessment** below contain the elements of a risk assessment and indicate the data needed for it to be undertaken, with indicative values.

Because many companies wishing to undertake risk assessment will not have ready access to experts, and such experts may not have all the information required for a quantitative risk assessment, the Table of values provided in this Appendix represents the likely ranges for the key determinants of risk. When using this questionnaire it is essential to remember that the Risk Profile (estimate) - its output - will only be as good as the data used in the assessment.

This Risk Profile will allow the user to recognise the features of the process and product exerting the biggest influence on the level of risk, to distinguish between the seriousness of various hazards and visualise the 'riskiness' of the product under examination.

Note: The Risk Profile will not (and cannot) give the detail obtained by carrying out a formal MRA

This Appendix contains four main sections:
- A general introduction to "The Simple Risk Profile"
- Risk Profile questions with commentary (for infective and toxigenic pathogens) and options for answers
- List of Suggested Levels - Tables of options used in the Risk Profile
- A set of three worked examples It is important to note that these examples are for illustrative purposes only and should not be regarded as actual risk assessments.

Instruction and advice on how to use the simple Risk Profile

The risk profile is presented as a series of questions (cf. Flow Diagram and Risk Assessment Form) which cover the steps of MRA except **Statement of Purpose** and **Formal Report** which play no part in the scientific aspects of the risk assessment.

The steps covered here are:
- Hazard Identification
- Exposure Assessment
- Hazard Characterisation
- Risk Characterisation.

Note: In this Appendix Step 4 Hazard Characterisation (Dose Response) is listed before Step 3 Exposure Assessment (the convention used in the rest of the document). This is done to emphasise that these two steps are normally considered in parallel rather than in any specific order.

Going through the Risk Profile considerations, it can be seen that each sub-step contributing to the risk profile can be rated from low to high.

For example:

- the frequency of occurrence of the hazard in the food from very low to very high.
- the concentration of microbial pathogens necessary to cause illness ranging from the less virulent pathogens (high dose required to cause illness) to the very virulent pathogens (which cause illness at very low doses).

The risk ratings can be replaced with numbers - low (1) to high (5). This approach is adopted in this Appendix, where the sub-steps of the Risk Profile are considered in turn and those of the steps of Hazard Characterisation and Exposure Assessment are rated from 1 to 5 in each case. (The list of levels, and commentary text can be used as guidance of what rating to adopt. Expert opinion, sources of information and relevant data can be consulted to make the rating adopted as accurate as possible.)

Hazard Identification

Food

The first thing to do when starting a Risk Assessment is to define which food or type of food is being considered by the Risk Assessment (e.g. poultry: chilled or frozen, raw or ready-to-eat). The food type and usage will determine the effect and importance of raw material, processing and consumer use on the type and level of pathogens.

Micro-organism

The micro-organisms of concern are pathogens commonly associated with the food. They may be in the raw materials (e.g. *Salmonella* in egg products) or introduced during processing and preparation (e.g. *Staphylococcus aureus*).

Hazard Characterisation

Population of concern

The population of concern is the group of consumers covered by the Risk Assessment. The Risk Assessment should try to identify realistic sub-groups within the whole population likely to eat the food. If these sub-groups have different sensitivities to the hazard, then the Risk Assessment should primarily focus on the most sensitive sub-group (e.g. children, immuno-compromised people) unless they can be specifically excluded.

Sensitivity and minimum dose

Differences in the sensitivity of populations and sub-populations depend on the nature of the pathogen and the food it is ingested with. The immune status and physiology of sub-populations, as well as the food itself, can alter infectivity, especially if the food protects the pathogens after ingestion. Hence in this Risk assessment the minimum dose is defined as the minimum number of micro-organism directly causing harm by infection or toxin production.

Exposure Assessment

This stage looks at what happens to the concentration of micro-organisms (and toxin if appropriate) from the raw material, through processing to consumption of the foods.

Toxigenic micro-organisms

At each step of the food chain, the fate of the toxin depends on the fate of the micro-organism. Stability of the toxin is not considered. The following table gives some indications of the relationship between the level of toxin and the fate of the toxin producer.

Is the toxigenic micro-organism present from previous steps?	**Is toxin present from previous steps?**	
	Yes	**No**
Yes	The level of toxin can : • increase, • stay the same, • decrease (denaturation)	The level of toxin can : • increase, • stay the same
No	The level of toxin can : • stay the same, • decrease (denaturation)	The level of toxin stays the same = 0

Portion size

Differences in portion size are not as large as those differences associated with the other factors in the Risk Assessment. Levels of contamination with pathogens and its frequency, changes in pathogen numbers prior to consumption, and the minimum hazardous number or dose can differ on a Log-scale, whereas differences in portion size are more linear. Therefore, if the hazard is proportional to the number of micro-organisms, then the effect of portion size is generally negligible.

However, if the hazard is the toxin produced by the micro-organism and response to the toxin is generally linear, then portion size needs to be considered by the Risk Assessment.

Interpretation of the risk profile

Risk profile

When all the questions on Hazard Characterisation and Exposure Assessment have been answered, the Risk Profile is made up of values between 1 and 5.

The higher the value, the higher the risk is, therefore if the risk profile consists mainly of 4 and 5, the risk associated with the micro-organism and the food is high, whereas if most of the steps of the Risk Assessment have a level of 1, the risk is small.

Fifteen questions refer to both infectious and toxigenic pathogens (maximum score for a very hazardous product, based on infectious pathogens is 75 (using simple addition of ratings and no weighting of answers). An additional six questions refer to toxigenisis - therefore for a toxigenic pathogen the maximum score would be 105).

Because the Risk Profile covers both infectious and toxin-producing micro-organisms, the toxigenic types produce responses to additional questions (shown in the **'risk profile - total score'**). A more realistic comparative score can be obtained if the **'risk profile comparable score'** is used when the severity of hazards is being compared. Where the reply to any question is a high score, there is a high risk at this stage in the food chain.

Quality of the information

Besides the 'risk profile' there is also an 'information quality profile'; this indicates the reliability of the risk profile. The higher the score, the higher the uncertainty, i.e. the greater the number of 1 and 2 scores in the replies on the quality of information, the more reliable the

Risk Assessment is likely to be. Where there are a significant number of scores with 4 or 5, effort needs to be put into providing better sources of information to improve the reliability of the Risk Assessment.

The uncertainty score is based on the response to 13 questions (in shaded boxes); therefore the maximum score for replies based entirely on opinion would be 65, and a Risk Profile based on qualitative information (or better) would score 39 or below. The minimum 'quality score' which could be obtained is 13.

These values emphasise the importance of the requirement for good quality data and information to carry out a Risk Assessment. If the data / information are poor, the uncertainty score is high and so the total score is high, indicating high risk which may not be merited.

To aid the use of the Risk Profile, some explanation of terms used is given here. The numbers in parentheses refer to the question number in the risk profile chart.

Toxigenic (e.g. 2.2) — The ability of a microorganism, e.g. *Staphylococcus aureus*, to produce toxin which can lead to food poisoning

Infective — Some microorganisms, e.g. *Salmonella* spp, are not able to produce a toxin, but are able to give rise to food poisoning by invading the host's body via the gut. These microorganisms are termed 'infective' pathogens.

Sensitivity (e.g. 3.3) — How vulnerable a potential host (individual) is to the hazard.

Mild symptoms (e.g. 3.3) — Slight discomfort, could include vomiting and diarrhoea followed by rapid recovery. Not ill enough to visit the GP.

Severe symptoms (e.g. 3.3) — Victim is laid low. Certainly serious enough to consult a GP.

Uncertainty (e.g. 3.5) — How realistic is the estimate. This will be reflected by the degree of confidence the risk assessors have in the data used.

Inactivation (e.g. 5.2) — Essentially 'killing'. The microorganisms are injured to an extent that they cannot recover.

Survival (e.g. 5.2)	The microorganism is still viable
Slow growth (e.g. 5.2)	Rate of growth by microorganisms when conditions (e.g. pH, temperature, etc) are not too hostile to stop growth altogether, but are not ideal. Different microorganisms require different conditions for growth. Therefore, given conditions may allow slow growth of some microorganisms, but rapid growth by others.
Rapid growth (e.g. 5.2)	A microorganism can grow rapidly when conditions (e.g. pH, temperature, etc) are close to optimal for that microorganism.
Frequency (e.g. 6.1)	How many times per batch (or per individual unit of food) after treatment is toxin found.

Key points to note when using the questionnaire

- A risk profile will not, and cannot, give the detail obtained from carrying out a formal MRA
- The questions to be addressed are numbered and grouped under appropriate headings (e.g. hazard identification, hazard authorisation)
- The definitions presented on the previous page can help to clarify the meaning of specific terms or that intended in the context of this exercise
- A list of suggested levels is provided in Section A2.3, to help in formulating and standardising the answers to these questions - especially with regards to specific ratings and rankings
- A distinction is made between the risk profile itself and the 'information quality policy' which indicates the reliability of the risk profile. To help distinguish these, the information 'quality profile' questions are lightly shaded.

A2.2 Risk Profile Questions with Commentary

Question	Commentary: Infectious pathogens	Commentary: Toxigenic pathogens	Type of answer
	Hazard Identification		
1. *What is the name and type of product?*	For example: cooked ham; canned low-acid food; raw/cooked poultry		Name and type of food
2. *What are the micro-organisms realistically associated with the product?*	For example: *Salmonella*	For example: *Staphylococcus aureus*	Names and types of micro-organisms
2.1 *What is the micro-organism covered by this risk assessment?*			Name of micro-organism
2.2 *Is it toxigenic or not?*	No	Yes	(Yes/No)
	Hazard Characterisation		
3.1 *Who are the consumers of concern?*	For example: Families/Babies/Elderly		Who is likely to consume the product?
3.2 *How many distinctive sub groups are there in the population of consumers?*			Number and description (e.g. a homogeneous group or containing 2 or 3 sub-populations with sensitivities). (The risk assessment will need to be run for each sub-population.)
3.3 *What is the severity of the hazard? (the sensitivity of each group should be considered or that of the most sensitive consumers should be used for a single assessment)*	Text book descriptions and information from specialist agencies on sensitivity and severity for typical/sensitive consumers of the product should be used		1. Mild symptoms, prompt recovery 2. Mild symptoms for a few days 3. Generally mild symptoms but some cases of hospitalisation 4. Severe symptoms, hospitalisation, some deaths 5. Death
3.4 *What is the hazardous level of the micro-organism covered by this risk assessment?*	The generally accepted infectious dose, boundaries of toxigenesis or toxin persistence should be used.		1. > 10^4 cells 2. High minimum dose : 1000-10^4 cells 3. Minimum dose : 100-1000 cells 4. Low minimum dose : 10-100 cells 5. Very low minimum dose : 0-10 cells

Question	Commentary Infectious pathogens Toxigenic pathogens	Type of answer
	Hazard Identification (continued)	
3.5 What is the uncertainty of this estimate?	There will be high uncertainty with this type of risk estimate, it will only be generally valid and take account of the consumers with 'text-book' sensitivity.	1. Accurate, precise data on relevant microbe and food 2. Accurate, precise data on similar microbe and food 3. Quantitative general information on similar microbe and food 4. Qualitative general information on similar microbe and food 5. Opinion / default, no hard data
	Exposure assessment (occurrence of the hazardous micro-organism)	
4.1 What is the frequency of contamination of the raw materials making-up the product?	In-house data can be gathered to determine frequency of contamination and levels of microorganisms. Levels deemed acceptable/ unacceptable need to be considered. Literature data may be used to derive these figures, in which case the data used needs to be recorded	1. Never 2. Very low frequency : 1/1000 3. Low frequency : 1/100 4. High frequency : 1/10 5. Always
4.2 What is the range of levels of contamination found in the raw materials?		1. 0-10 cells/g 2. 0-10^2 cells/g 3. 0-10^3 cells/g 4. 0-10^4 cells/g 5. >10^4 cells/g
4.3 How uncertain is this estimate?	Any sources used to arrive at decisions on this need to be recorded. If expert opinion has been used, the name of the expert must be recorded	1. Accurate, precise data on relevant microbe and food 2. Accurate, precise data on similar microbe and food 3. Quantitative general information on similar microbe and food 4. Qualitative general information on similar microbe and food 5. Opinion / default, no hard data

Question	Commentary: Infectious pathogens	Commentary: Toxigenic pathogens	Type of answer
	Exposure assessment (effect of processing/decontamination)		
5.1 *What is the effect of storage before processing on the level of the hazard?*	Data used or expert opinion derived must be recorded		1. 0-10 cells/g 2. 0-10^2 cells/g 3. 0-10^3 cells/g 4. 0-10^4 cells/g 5. >10^4 cells/g
5.2 *What is the intended effect of all processing and any decontamination stages on the level of the micro-organism?*	The presence of hazards in raw materials and likely effect of the 'supply and use' chain on numbers (unchanged, increase or decrease) must be noted. All assumptions must be clearly stated with accompanying reasoning. Where process (eg. pasteurisation) or storage/use conditions have a defined purpose this must be stated, with the likely number of survivors. Where there is no data, the presence or survival of the hazard at a hazardous dose at consumption must be assumed. For example, pasteurisation (70°C for 2 mins) eliminated infectious pathogens and hygienic cooling prevented recontamination.	The chances of presence of toxin in raw materials and effect of supply chain and use conditions (raw material, process or product) on its production should be estimated. All assumptions must be clearly stated with accompanying reasoning. If the effect of the 'supply and use' chain are unknown and the presence of toxin producers is a a realistic hazard, then the presence of toxin in the product should be assumed. For example, raw materials containing less than 10^4 *Staphylococcus aureus*/g were used and the product A_w was reduced to below 0.93 within 4h at <20°C. Toxigenisis was not considered a risk.	1. Inactivation : At least 6-log decrease in numbers 2. Inactivation : between 3 and 6-log decrease in numbers 3. No changes : Survival. 4. Slow Growth : Less than 3-log increase in numbers 5. Rapid growth : At least 3-log increase in numbers
5.3 *What is the uncertainty of this estimate?*	High levels of uncertainty may be associated with this type of assessment, making it more-or-less useless - for example if the product is safe with high uncertainty. Default conditions offering the highest level of consumer protection should be used.		1. Accurate, precise data on relevant microbe and food 2. Accurate, precise data on similar microbe and food 3. Quantitative general information on similar microbe and food 4. Qualitative general information on similar microbe and food 5. Opinion / default, no hard data

Question	Commentary — Infectious pathogens	Commentary — Toxigenic pathogens	Type of answer
Exposure assessment - Occurrence of toxin (if the hazardous micro-organism is toxigenic)			
6.1 *What is the likelihood of toxin presence if the micro-organism can produce toxin and contaminates the raw materials or product?*	None	The conditions for toxin production need to be known to assess this. Sources of information must be recorded.	1. Never 2. Very low frequency : 1/1000 3. Low frequency : 1/100 4. High frequency : 1/10 5. Always
6.2 *What is the uncertainty of this estimate?*			1. Accurate, precise data on relevant microbe and food 2. Accurate, precise data on similar microbe and food 3. Quantitative general information on similar microbe and food 4. Qualitative general information on similar microbe and food 5. Opinion / default, no hard data
Exposure assessment - Re-contamination after processing or decontamination			
7.1 *What is the frequency of re-contamination of the product in the factory after processing or decontamination, so that the hazard is present in the final product?*	If in-house assessment of mathematical modelling has been used to assess this, for example, the detail needs to be recorded		1. Never 2. Very low frequency : 1/1000 3. Low frequency : 1/100 4. High frequency : 1/10 5. Always
7.2 *What is the likely level of re-contamination after processing or decontamination?*	If in-house assessment of mathematical modelling has been used to assess this, for example, the detail needs to be recorded		1. 0-10 cells/g 2. 0-10^2 cells/g 3. 0-10^3 cells/g 4. 0-10^4 cells/g 5. >10^4 cells/g
7.3 *What is the uncertainty of this estimate?*			1. Accurate, precise data on relevant microbe and food 2. Accurate, precise data on similar microbe and food 3. Quantitative general information on similar microbe and food 4. Qualitative general information on similar microbe and food 5. Opinion / default, no hard data

Question	Commentary Infectious pathogens Toxigenic pathogens	Type of answer
	Exposure assessment - Packaging	
8.1 *Is the product put in its primary packaging before **(yes)** or after **(no)** decontamination step?*		Yes (**before**) / No (**after**)
8.2 If the answer to 8.1 is yes (before), what is the effectiveness of packaging in preventing recontamination before consumption?		
8.3 *Frequency of recontamination after packaging*		0. Not applicable 1. Never 2. Very low frequency : 1/1000 3. Low frequency : 1/100 4. High frequency : 1/10 5. Always
8.4 *Amount of recontamination after packaging*	This can be assessed best by in-house testing, in which case the results need to be recorded	0. Not applicable 1. 0-10 cells/g 2. 0-10^2 cells/g 3. 0-10^3 cells/g 4. 0-10^4 cells/g 5. >10^4 cells/g
8.5 *Uncertainty of estimate*		0. Not applicable 1. Accurate, precise data on relevant microbe and food 2. Accurate, precise data on similar microbe and food 3. Quantitative general information on similar microbe and food 4. Qualitative general information on similar microbe and food 5. Opinion / default, no hard data
	Exposure assessment - Effect of storage	
9.1 *How does the level of the microorganism change during storage?*	Data used or expert opinion derived must be recorded	1. Inactivation : At least 6-log decrease in numbers 2. Inactivation : between 3 and 6-log decrease in numbers 3. No change: Survival. 4. Slow Growth : Less than 3-log increase in numbers 5. Rapid growth : At least 3-log increase in numbers

Question	Commentary Infectious pathogens Toxigenic pathogens	Type of answer
	Exposure assessment - Effect of storage (continued)	
9.2 *What is the uncertainty of this estimate?*		1. Accurate, precise data on relevant microbe and food 2. Accurate, precise data on similar microbe and food 3. Quantitative general information on similar microbe and food 4. Qualitative general information on similar microbe and food 5. Opinion / default, no hard data
9.3 *What is the effect of storage of the final product (according to the usage instructions) on the level of toxin?*	Data used or expert opinion derived must be recorded How does storage of the product throughout the chain from production to consumption affect the hazard.	1. Large reduction : At least 6-log decrease in numbers 2. Small reduction : between 3 and 6-log decrease in numbers 3. No change : survival 4. Small increase : between 3 and 6-log increase in numbers 5. Large increase : At least 6-log decrease in numbers
9.4 *What is the effect of storage conditions on toxigenesis (If the level of the micro-organism changes and it is toxigenic)*		0. Not applicable 1. Inactivation : At least 6-log decrease in numbers - no toxin production 2. Inactivation : between 3 and 6-log decrease in numbers - no toxin production 3. No changes : Survival - no toxin production 4. Slow Growth : Less than 3-log increase in numbers - low chance of toxin production 5. Rapid growth : At least 3-log increase in numbers - high chance of toxin production
9.5 *What is the likelihood of toxigenesis in the product?*	Consideration needs to be given to the conditions reported in the literature which give rise to toxin production, and how these are reflected by the foods.	0. Not applicable 1. Never 2. Unlikely 3. Possible 4. Likely 5. Certain

Question	Commentary Infectious pathogens Toxigenic pathogens	Type of answer
	Exposure assessment - Effect of storage (continued)	
9.6 What is the uncertainty of this estimate?		1. Accurate, precise data on relevant microbe and food 2. Accurate, precise data on similar microbe and food 3. Quantitative general information on similar microbe and food 4. Qualitative general information on similar microbe and food 5. Opinion/ default, no hard data
	Exposure assessment - Consumer use	
*10.1 Is the product intended as single use (**yes**) or multi-use (**no**), where it will be stored after opening?*	Assessment should be based on storage, use or portion size instructions, unless there is data to suggest that other practices can significantly alter risk or dose (e.g. undercooking). Public health data may be used to increase knowledge of likely abuse conditions and risks. For example, storage below 10°C, use within 3 days, portion size 50g, cook 5 mins under medium heat.	Yes (single use) /No (multi-use)
10.2 If the answer to 10.1. is No, this means that the product is multi-use either in a domestic or food service application and 11 & 12 must be completed.		
	Exposure assessment - The effect of open shelf life on the microbial hazard	
11.1 What is the effect of open shelf-life storage on the level of micro-organisms?	This can be assessed by consideration of growth conditions for the hazard, and how they are reflected by the conditions presented by the food.	1. Inactivation : At least 6-log decrease in numbers 2. Inactivation : between 3 and 6-log decrease in numbers 3. No changes: Survival. 4. Slow Growth : Less than 3-log increase in numbers 5. Rapid growth : At least 3-log increase in numbers

Question	Commentary Infectious pathogens Toxigenic pathogens	Type of answer
Exposure assessment - The effect of open shelf life on the microbial hazard (continued)		
11.2 What is the uncertainty of this estimate?		1. Accurate, precise data on relevant microbe and food 2. Accurate, precise data on similar microbe and food 3. Quantitative general information on similar microbe and food 4. Qualitative general information on similar microbe and food 5. Opinion / default, no hard data
Exposure assessment - The effect of open shelf life on toxigenesis		
12.1 What is the likelihood of growth and toxin production during open shelf life?		1. Inactivation : At least 6-log decrease in numbers - no toxin production 2. Inactivation : between 3 and 6-log decrease in numbers - no toxin production 3. No changes : Survival - no toxin production 4. Slow Growth : Less than 3-log increase in numbers - low chance of toxin production 5. Rapid growth : At least 3-log increase in numbers - high chance of toxin production
12.2 What is the uncertainty of this estimate?		1. Accurate, precise data on relevant microbe and food 2. Accurate, precise data on similar microbe and food 3. Quantitative general information on similar microbe and food 4. Qualitative general information on similar microbe and food 5. Opinion / default, no hard data

Question	Commentary Infectious pathogens Toxigenic pathogens	Type of answer
Exposure assessment - The effect of usage and preparation on hazards		
13.1 What is the effect of customer or food service preparation and usage on the level of hazard?	Assessment should be based on storage, use or portion size instructions, unless there is data to suggest that other practices can significantly alter risk or dose (e.g. undercooking). Public health data may be used to increase knowledge of likely abuse conditions and risks. For example, storage below 10°C, use within 3 days, portion size 50g, cook 5 mins under medium heat.	1. Inactivation : At least 6-log decrease in numbers 2. Inactivation : between 3 and 6-log decrease in numbers 3. No changes: Survival. 4. Slow Growth : Less than 3-log increase in numbers 5. Rapid growth : At least 3-log increase in numbers
13.2 What is the uncertainty of this estimate?		1. Accurate, precise data on relevant microbe and food 2. Accurate, precise data on similar microbe and food 3. Quantitative general information on similar microbe and food 4. Qualitative general information on similar microbe and food 5. Opinion/default, no hard data
13.3. What is the effect of usage and preparation on toxin level and production?		0. Not Applicable 1. Eliminate 2. Reduce 3. Unchanged 4. Slight increase 5. Large increase
13.4 What is the probability of toxin presence at the point of consumption?		0. Not Applicable 1. Never 2. Very low frequency : 1/1000 3. Low frequency : 1/100 4. High frequency : 1/10 5. Always
13.5 What is the uncertainty of this estimate?		0. Not applicable 1. Accurate, precise data on relevant microbe and food 2. Accurate, precise data on similar microbe and food 3. Quantitative general information on similar microbe and food 4. Qualitative general information on similar microbe and food 5. Opinion/default, no hard data

Question	Commentary Infectious pathogens Toxigenic pathogens	Type of answer
Exposure assessment - Food intake by a consumer		
14.1 What is the likely quantity of the food consumed by a customer on a specified occasion or over a period of time?		1. Very low intake : 0-10 g 2. Low intake : 10-50g 3. Medium intake : 50-100g 4. High intake : 100-200g 5. Very high intake : >200g
14.2 What is the uncertainty of this estimate?		1. Accurate, precise data on relevant microbe and food 2. Accurate, precise data on similar microbe and food 3. Quantitative general information on similar microbe and food 4. Qualitative general information on similar microbe and food 5. Opinion / default, no hard data

A2.3 Suggested List of Levels

Hazards
For use with question 2.1

Aeromonas
Amoeba
*Bacillus cereus**
Bacillus licheniformis
Bacillus subtilis
Brucella
Campylobacter
*Clostridium botulinum**
*Clostridium perfringens**
Cryptosporidium
Cyclospora
Escherichia coli (pathogenic non O157)
E.coli O157
Giardia
Helicobacter
Listeria monocytogenes
Moulds (Mycotoxins)*
Mycobacterium
Plesiomonas
Salmonella
Salmonella paratyphi
Salmonella typhi
Shigella
*Staphylococcus aureus**
Streptococcus
Vibrio

*Known to cause illness through toxin production.

Severity of the hazard
For use with question 3.3

1. Mild symptoms, prompt recovery
2. Mild symptoms for a few days
3. Generally mild symptoms but some case of hospitalisation
4. Severe symptoms, hospitalisation, some deaths
5. Death

***Nb.** Not Applicable = 0 in all questions*

Minimum Dose
For use with question 3.4

1. Very High (e.g. >10,000 cells)
2. High (e.g. 1,000-10,000 cells)
3. Medium (e.g. 100-1,000 cells)
4. Low (e.g. 10-100 cells)
5. Very Low (e.g. <10 cells)

Quality of the information (Uncertainty)
For use with questions 3.5, 4.3, 6.2, 7.3, 8.5, 9.2, 9.6, 11.2, 12.2, 13.2, 13.5, 14.2

1. Very good confidence in the data/information
2. Good confidence in the data/info but some uncertainty
3. Reasonable confidence in the data/information
4. Little confidence in the data/information
5. Opinion / default, no hard data

Frequency of contamination
For use with questions 4.1, 6.1, 7.1, 8.3

1. Negligible (0-0.1%)
2. Very Low Frequency (0-1%)
3. Low Frequency (1-10%)
4. Mid Frequency (10-50%)
5. Frequent (50-100%)

Contamination levels
For use with question 4.2, 5.1, 7.2, 8.4

1. 0-10 cells/g
2. 0-100 cells/g
3. 0-1,000 cells/g
4. 0-10,000 cells/g
5. > 10,0000 cells/g

Effect of process step
For use with questions 5.2, 9.1, 9.3, 11.1, 12.1, 13.1

1. Complete Inactivation (e.g. pasteurisation or sterilisation)
2. Partial Inactivation
3. Survival : No changes in numbers
4. Some Growth (small increase in numbers)
5. Growth : Large increase in numbers

Effect of process step on toxin
For use with questions 6.1, 9.4, 9.5, 12.1, 13.3, 13.4

1. Complete denaturation of the toxin
2. Partial denaturation of the toxin
3. No changes
4. Some toxin production
5. Large amount of toxin produced

Size of the portion
Q : 14.1
1. Very Low Intake : 0-10g
2. Low Intake : 10-50g
3. Medium Intake : 50-100g
4. High Intake : 100-200g
5. Very High Intake : > 200g

A2.4 Risk profile examples

Example 1 - *Staph. aureus* and *Listeria monocytogenes* in cooked ham

Warning - these are examples only

Ratings (1-5) are given in bold, those associated with quality of information (uncertainty) are in shaded boxes and are added separately at the end to give the 'information quality profile'

Question	**Risk assessment 1**	**Risk assessment 2**
Hazard Identification		
1. What is the name and type of product?	Cooked ham	Cooked ham
2. What are the micro-organisms realistically associated with the product?	*Listeria monocytogenes*, *Staphylococcus aureus*, *Salmonella* Typhimurium	*Listeria monocytogenes*, *Staphylococcus aureus*, *Salmonella* Typhimurium
2.1 What is the micro-organism covered by this risk assessment?	*Staphylococcus aureus*	*Listeria monocytogenes*
2.2 Is it toxigenic or not ?	Yes	No
Hazard Characterisation		
3.1 Who are the consumers of concern ?	Families	Families
3.2 How many distinctive sub-groups are there in the population of consumers?	Children, adults, the old.	Pregnant women, immuno-compromised
3.3 What is the severity of the hazard (the sensitivity of each group should be considered or that of the most sensitive consumers should be used for a single assessment)?	**3** Generally, mild symptoms but some case of hospitalisation	**4** Severe symptoms, hospitalisation some deaths
3.4 What is the hazardous level of the micro-organism covered by this risk assessment?	**1** more than 10^4 cells	**4** Low minimum dose : 10-100 cells
3.5 What is the uncertainty of this estimate?	**3** Quantitative general - information on similar microbe and food	**1** Accurate, precise data on relevant microbe and food
Exposure assessment (occurrence of the hazardous micro-organism)		
4.1 What is the frequency of contamination of the raw materials making up the product?	**3** Low frequency : 1/100	**5** Always
4.2 What is the range of levels of contamination found in the raw materials?	**3** 0-10^3 cells/g	**4** 0-10^4 cells/g
4.3 How uncertain is this estimate?	**4** Qualitative general information on similar microbe and food	**4** Qualitative general information on similar microbe and food

Question	**Risk assessment 1**	**Risk assessment 2**
Exposure assessment - Effect of processing/decontamination		
5.1 *What is the effect of storage before processing on the level of the hazard?*	**3** 0-10^3 cells/g	**5** more than 10^4 cells/g
5.2 *What is the intended effect of all processing and any decontamination stages on the level of the micro-organism?*	**1** Inactivation: At least 6-log decrease in numbers for both microorganisms	**1** Inactivation: At least 6-log decrease in numbers for both microorganisms
5.3 *What is the uncertainty of this estimate?*	**1** Accurate, precise data on similar microbe and food	**1** Accurate, precise data on similar microbe and food
Exposure assessment - Occurrence of toxin (if the hazardous micro-organism is toxigenic)		
6.1 *What is the likelihood of toxin presence if the micro-organism contaminates the raw materials or product?*	**3** Low frequency : 1/100	N/a
6.2 *What is the uncertainty of this estimate?*	**5** Opinion / default, no hard data	N/a
Exposure assessment - Re-contamination after processing or decontamination		
7.1 *What is the frequency of re-contamination of the product in the factory after processing or decontamination, so that the hazard is present in the final product?*	**2** Very low frequency : 1/1000	**2** Very low frequency : 1/1000
7.2 *What is the likely level of re-contamination after processing or decontamination?*	**2** 0-10^2 cells/g	**1** 0-10 cells/g
7.3 *What is the uncertainty of this estimate?*	**1** Accurate precise data on similar microbe and food	**1** Accurate precise data on similar microbe and food
Exposure assessment - Packaging		
8.1 *Is the product put in its primary packaging before* ***(yes)*** *or after* ***(no)*** *the decontamination step ?*	No (after)	No (after)
8.2 *If the answer to 8.1 is* ***yes****- what is the effectiveness of packaging at preventing recontamination before consumption?*	N/a	N/a
8.3 *What is the frequency of recontamination after packaging?*	**1** Never	**1** Never

Question	**Risk assessment 1**	**Risk assessment 2**
8.4 What is the level of recontamination after packaging?	**1** 0 - 10 cells/g	**1** 0 - 10 cells/g
8.5 What is the uncertainty of the estimate?	**1** Accurate precise data on similar microbe and food	**1** Accurate precise data on similar microbe and food
Exposure assessment - Effect of product storage		
9.1 How does the level of the microorganism change during product storage?	**3** No change: survival.	**4** Slow growth : less than 3 log increase in numbers
9.2 What is the uncertainty of this estimate?	**3** Quantitative general information on similar microbe and food	**3** Quantitative general information on similar microbe and food
9.3 What is the effect of storage of the final product (according to the usage instructions) on the level of toxin?	**3** No change : survival	**4** Slow growth : less than 3 log increase in numbers
9.4 What is the effect of storage conditions on toxigenesis (If the level of the micro-organism changes and it is toxigenic)	**3** No change : survival - no toxin production	N/a
9.5 What is the likelihood of toxigenesis in the product?	**3** Possible	N/a
9.6 What is the uncertainty of this estimate?	**4** Qualitative general information on similar microbe and food	**4** Qualitative general information on similar microbe and food
Exposure assessment - Consumer use		
*10.1 Is the product intended as single use **(yes)** or multi-use **(no)**, with storage after opening?*	No	No
10.2 If the answer to 10.1. is No, this means that the product is multi-use either in a domestic or food service application, and sections 11 & 12 must be completed.		
Exposure assessment - The effect of open shelf-life on the microbial hazard		
11.1 What is the effect of open shelf-life storage on the level of micro-organisms ?	**3** No change - survival	**4** Slow growth : Less than 3-log increase in numbers
11.2 What is the uncertainty of this estimate?	**5** Opinion / default, no hard data	**1** Accurate precise data on similar microbe and food

Question	**Risk assessment 1**	**Risk assessment 2**
Exposure assessment - The effect of open shelf-life on toxigenesis		
12.1 What is the likelihood of growth and toxin production during open shelf-life?	**4** Slow growth: Less than 3-log increase in numbers - low chance of toxin production	N/a
12.2 What is the uncertainty of this estimate?	**4** Qualitative general information on similar microbe and food	N/a
Exposure assessment - The effect of usage and preparation on the level of the hazardous micro-organisms		
13.1 What is the effect of customer or food service preparation and usage on the level of hazard?	**3** No changes : survival.	**4** Slow growth : Less than 3-log increase in numbers
13.2 What is the uncertainty of this estimate?	**5** Opinion / default, no hard data	**5** Opinion / default, no hard data
13.3 What is the effect of usage and preparation on toxin level and production?	**3** Unchanged	N/a
13.4 What is the probability of toxin presence at the point of consumption?	**2** Very low frequency : 1/1000	N/a
13.5 What is the uncertainty of this estimate?	**5** Opinion, no hard data	N/a
Exposure assessment - Food intake by a consumer		
14.1 What is the likely quantity of the food consumed by a customer on a specified occasion or over a period of time?	**3** Medium intake : 50-100g	**3** Medium intake : 50-100g
14.2 What is the uncertainty of this estimate?	**3** Quantitative general information on similar microbe and food	**3** Quantitative general information on similar microbe and food
Risk profile - total 'score' **Risk profile - comparable 'score'- excluding toxin specific scores**	**53** **35** **Excluding score from** 6.1, 9.4, 9.5, 12.1, 13.3, 13.4	**47** **47**
Information quality profile	**44**	**24**

The scores indicate that for this production line, cooked ham is more at risk from *Staphylococcus aureus* than from *Listeria monocytogenes* (53 compared with 47) and the level of uncertainty surrounding the risk profile is higher (44 compared with 24). From the distribution of 'scores' *Listeria monocytogenes* represents the more serious hazard (47 compared with 35).

Example 2 - *Staphylococcus aureus* and *Clostridium botulinum* in canned low-acid food

Warning - these are examples only

Ratings (1-5) are given in bold, those associated with quality of information (uncertainty) are in shaded boxes and are added separately at the end to give the 'information quality profile'

Question		**Risk assessment 1**	**Risk assessment 2**
Hazard Identification			
1.	*What is the name and type of product?*	Canned low acid food	Canned low acid food
2	*What are the micro-organisms realistically associated with the product?*	*Staphylococcus aureus* - from wet pack handling, *Clostridium botulinum*	*Staphylococcus aureus* - from wet pack handling, *Clostridium botulinum*
2.1	*What is the micro-organism covered by this risk assessment?*	*Staphylococcus aureus*	*Clostridium botulinum*
2.2.	*Is it toxigenic or not ?*	Yes	Yes
Hazard Characterisation			
3.1	*Who are the consumers of concern ?*	Families	Families
3.2	*How many distinctive sub-groups are there in the population of consumers?*	N/a	N/a
3.3	*What is the severity of the hazard (the sensitivity of each group should be considered or that of the most sensitive consumers should be used for a single assessment)?*	**3** Generally, mild symptoms but some cases of hospitalisation	**5** Death
3.4	*What is the hazardous level of the micro-organism covered by this risk assessment?*	**1** $>10^4$ cells	**5** Very low minimum dose : 0-10 cells
3.5	*What is the uncertainty of this estimate?*	**3** Quantitative general information on similar microbe and food	**1** Accurate, precise data on relevant microbe and food
Exposure assessment (occurrence of the hazardous micro-organism)			
4.1	*What is the frequency of contamination of the raw materials making up the product?*	**3** Low frequency : 1/100	**5** Always
4.2	*What is the range of levels of contamination found in the raw materials?*	**3** 0-10^3 cells/g	**4** 0-10^2 cells/g
4.3	*How uncertain is this estimate?*	**4** Qualitative general information on similar microbe and food	**4** Qualitative general information on similar microbe and food

Question	**Risk assessment 1**	**Risk assessment 2**
Exposure assessment - Effect of processing/decontamination		
5.1 What is the effect of storage before processing on the level of the hazard?	**3** 0-10^3 cells/g	**4** 0-10^2 cells/g
5.2 *What is the intended effect of all processing and any decontamination stages on the level of the micro-organism?*	**1** Inactivation : At least 6-log decrease in numbers	**1** Inactivation : At least 6-log decrease in numbers
5.3 What is the uncertainty of this estimate?	**1** Accurate, precise data on similar microbe and food	**1** Accurate, precise data on relevant microbe and food
Exposure assessment - Occurrence of toxin (if the hazardous micro-organism is toxigenic)		
6.1 What is the likelihood of toxin presence if the micro-organism contaminates the raw materials or product?	**3** Low frequency : 1/100	**4** High frequency 1/10
6.2 What is the uncertainty of this estimate?	**5** Opinion / default, no hard data	**1** Accurate, precise data on similar microbe and food
Exposure assessment - Re-contamination after processing or decontamination		
7.1 What is the frequency of re-contamination of the product in the factory after processing or decontamination, so that the hazard is present in the final product?	**2** Very low frequency : 1/1000	**1** Never
7.2 What is the likely level of re-contamination after processing or decontamination?	**2** 0-10^2 cells/g	**1** 0-10 cells/g
7.3 What is the uncertainty of this estimate?	**1** Accurate precise data on similar microbe and food	**1** Accurate, precise data on relevant microbe and food
Exposure assessment - Packaging		
*8.1 Is the product put in its primary packaging before **(yes)** or after **(no)** the decontamination step ?*	Yes	Yes
*8.2 If the answer to 8.1 is **yes**- what is the effectiveness of packaging at preventing recontamination before consumption?*	No rating for this answer	No rating for this answer
8.3 What is the frequency of recontamination after packaging?	**2** Very low frequency : 1/1000	**1** Never

Question	**Risk assessment 1**	**Risk assessment 2**
8.4 What is the level of recontamination after packaging?	**1** 0 - 10 cells/g	**1** 0 - 10 cells/g
8.5 What is the uncertainty of the estimate?	**1** Accurate precise data on relevant microbe and food	**1** Accurate precise data on relevant microbe and food
Exposure assessment - Effect of product storage		
9.1 How does the level of the microorganism change during product storage?	**3** No change: Survival.	**3** (**5** rapid growth: at least 3 log increase in numbers?)
9.2 What is the uncertainty of this estimate?	**3** Quantitative general information on similar microbe and food	**3** Quantitative general information on similar microbe and food
9.3 What is the effect of storage of the final product (according to the usage instructions) on the level of toxin?	**3** No change : survival	**3** (**5** rapid growth : at least 3 log increase in numbers?)
9.4 What is the effect of storage conditions on toxigenesis (If the level of the micro-organism changes and it is toxigenic)	**3** No change : Survival - no toxin production	**5** rapid growth : at least 3 log increase in numbers
9.5 What is the likelihood of toxigenesis in the product?	**3** Possible	**4** likely
9.6 What is the uncertainty of this estimate?	**4** Qualitative general information on similar microbe and food	**4** Qualitative general information on similar microbe and food
Exposure assessment - Consumer use		
*10.1 Is the product intended as single use (**yes**) or multi-use (**no**), with storage after opening?*	No	No
10.2 If the answer to 10.1. is No, this means that the product is multi-use either in a domestic or food service application, and sections 11 & 12 must be completed.		
Exposure assessment - The effect of open shelf-life on the microbial hazard		
11.1 What is the effect of open shelf life storage on the level of micro-organisms ?	**3** No change - survival	**4** Slow growth : Less than 3-log increase in numbers
11.2 What is the uncertainty of this estimate?	**5** Opinion / default, no hard data	**5** Opinion / default, no hard data

Question	**Risk assessment 1**	**Risk assessment 2**
Exposure assessment - The effect of open shelf-life on toxigenesis		
12.1 What is the likelihood of growth and toxin production during open shelf-life?	**4** Slow Growth: Less than 3-log increase in numbers - low chance of toxin production	**4** Slow Growth: Less than 3-log increase in numbers - low chance of toxin production
12.2 What is the uncertainty of this estimate?	**4** Qualitative general information on similar microbe and food	**4** Qualitative general information on similar microbe and food
Exposure assessment - The effect of usage and preparation on the level of the hazardous micro-organisms		
13.1 What is the effect of customer or food service preparation and usage on the level of hazard?	**3** No changes : Survival.	**3** No changes: survival
13.2 What is the uncertainty of this estimate	**5** Opinion/default, no hard data	**5** Opinion/default, no hard data
13.3 What is the effect of usage and preparation on toxin level and production?	**3** Unchanged	**3** Unchanged
13.4 What is the probability of toxin presence at the point of consumption?	**2** Very low frequency : 1/1000	**3** Low frequency 1/100
13.5 What is the uncertainty of this estimate	**5** Opinion, no hard data	**5** Opinion, no hard data
Exposure assessment - Food intake by a consumer		
14.1 What is the likely quantity of the food consumed by a customer on a specified occasion or over a period of time?	**3** Medium intake : 50-100g	**3** Medium intake : 50-100g
14.2 What is the uncertainty of this estimate?	**3** Quantitative general information on similar microbe and food	**3** Quantitative general information on similar microbe and food
Risk profile - total 'score' **Information quality profile**	**54** **44**	**67** **39**

The risks of *Clostridium botulinum* (67) are very much affected by the chances of survival and re-contamination. If this is considered, then it is recognised as a very serious hazard. The quality of information available for *Clostridium botulinum* is better than for *Staphylococcus aureus* (39 compared with 44).

Example 3 - *Salmonella* in frozen raw and fully cooked poultry

Warning - these are examples only

Ratings (1-5) are given in bold, those associated with quality of information (uncertainty) are in shaded boxes and are added separately at the end to give the 'information quality profile'

Question	**Risk assessment 1**	**Risk assessment 2**
Hazard Identification		
1. What is the name and type of product?	Frozen raw poultry	Fully cooked, frozen product
2. What are the micro-organisms realistically associated with the product?	*Salmonella* and *Campylobacter*	*Salmonella* and *Campylobacter*
2.1 What is the micro-organism covered by this risk assessment?	*Salmonella*	*Salmonella*
2.2. Is it toxigenic or not ?	No	No
Hazard Characterisation		
3.1 Who are the consumers of concern ?	Families, young and old people	Families, young and old people
3.2 How many distinctive sub-groups are there in the population of consumers?	N/a	N/a
3.3 What is the severity of the hazard (the sensitivity of each group should be considered or that of the most sensitive consumers should be used for a single assessment)?	**3** Generally, mild symptoms but some cases of hospitalisation	**3** Generally, mild symptoms but some cases of hospitalisation
3.4 What is the hazardous level of the micro-organism covered by this risk assessment?	**4** Low minimum dose 10-100 cells	**4** Low minimum dose 10-100 cells
3.5 What is the uncertainty of this estimate?	**4** Qualitative general information on similar microbe and food	**4** Qualitative general information on similar microbe and food
Exposure assessment (occurrence of the hazardous micro-organism)		
4.1 What is the frequency of contamination of the raw materials making-up the product?	**5** Always	**5** Always
4.2 What is the range of levels of contamination found in the raw materials?	**4** 0-10^4 cells/g	**4** 0-10^4 cells/g
4.3 How uncertain is this estimate?	**4** Qualitative general information on similar microbe and food	**4** Qualitative general information on similar microbe and food

Question	**Risk assessment 1**	**Risk assessment 2**
Exposure assessment - Effect of processing/decontamination		
5.1 What is the effect of storage before processing on the level of the hazard?	**4** 0-10^4 cells/g	**4** 0-10^4 cells/g
5.2. What is the intended effect of all processing and any decontamination stages on the level of the micro-organism?	**3** Survival	**1** Inactivation : At least 6 log decrease in numbers
5.3 What is the uncertainty of this estimate?	**3** Quantitative general information on similar microbe and food	**1** Accurate, precise data on relevant microbe and food
Exposure assessment - Occurrence of toxin (if the hazardous micro-organism is toxigenic)		
6.1 What is the likelihood of toxin presence if the micro-organism contaminates the raw materials or product?	N/a	N/a
6.2 What is the uncertainty of this estimate?		
Exposure assessment - Re-contamination after processing or decontamination		
7.1 What is the frequency of re-contamination of the product in the factory after processing or decontamination, so that the hazard is present in the final product?	**3** Low frequency : 1/100	**1** Never
7.2 What is the likely level of re-contamination after processing or decontamination?	**4** 0-10^4 cells/g	**1** 0-10 cells/g
7.3 What is the uncertainty of this estimate?	**3** Quantitative data on similar microbe and food	**1** Accurate, precise data on relevant microbe and food
Exposure assessment - Packaging		
*8.1 Is the product put in its primary packaging before **(yes)** or after **(no)** the decontamination step ?*	No	No
*8.2 If the answer to 8.1 is **yes**- what is the effectiveness of packaging at preventing recontamination before consumption?*	N/a	N/a
8.3 What is the frequency of recontamination after packaging?	**2** Very low frequency : 1/1000	**1** Never

Question	**Risk assessment 1**	**Risk assessment 2**
8.4 What is the level of recontamination after packaging?	**4** 0-10^4 cells/g	**1** 0 - 10 cells/g
8.5 What is the uncertainty of the estimate?	**3** Quantitative data on similar microbe and food	**1** Accurate precise data on relevant microbe and food
Exposure assessment - Effect of product storage		
9.1 How does the level of the microorganism change during product storage?	**3** No change: Survival	**3** No change: Survival
9.2 What is the uncertainty of this estimate?	**1** Accurate precise data on relevant microbe and food	**1** Accurate precise data on relevant microbe and food
9.3 What is the effect of storage of the final product (according to the usage instructions) on the level of toxin?	**3** No change : survival	**3** No change : survival
9.4 What is the effect of storage conditions on toxigenesis (If the level of the micro-organism changes and it is toxigenic)	N/a	N/a
9.5 What is the likelihood of toxigenesis in the product?		
9.6 What is the uncertainty of this estimate?		
Exposure assessment - Consumer use		
10.1 Is the product intended as single use ***(yes)****or multi-use* ***(no)****, with storage after opening?*	Yes	Yes
10.2 If the answer to 10.1. is No, this means that the product is multi-use either in a domestic or food service application, and sections 11 & 12 must be completed.		
Exposure assessment - The effect of open shelf-life on the microbial hazard		
11.1 What is the effect of open shelf-life storage on the level of micro-organisms ?		
11.2 What is the uncertainty of this estimate?		

Question	**Risk assessment 1**	**Risk assessment 2**
Exposure assessment - The effect of open shelf-life on toxigenesis		
12.1 What is the likelihood of growth and toxin production during open shelf-life?		
12.2 What is the uncertainty of this estimate?		
Exposure assessment - The effect of usage and preparation on the level of the hazardous micro-organisms		
13.1 What is the effect of customer or food service preparation and usage on the level of hazard?		
13.2 What is the uncertainty of this estimate?		
13.3 What is the effect of usage and preparation on toxin level and production?	N/a	N/a
13.4 What is the probability of toxin presence at the point of consumption?		
13.5 What is the uncertainty of this estimate?		
Exposure assessment - Food intake by a consumer		
14.1 What is the likely quantity of the food consumed by a customer on a specified occasion or over a period of time?		
14.2 What is the uncertainty of this estimate?		
Risk profile - total 'score'	**42**	**31**
Information quality profile	**17**	**12**

The chances of poultry containing infectious doses of *Salmonella* is considered by this quick risk assessment. Compared with the 'Cooked ham' (example 1) quick risk assessment, the uncertainty is lower. The risks associated with frozen raw poultry are high, because of the incidence in the raw material and the reliance on 'usage and preparation' for safety. When the product is cooked during manufacture, the risk is lower because heat processing and the prevention of re-contamination reduce numbers of *Salmonella* surviving the processing chain and hence the importance of customer cooking is also reduced.